Also by Brian O'Brien

BEATING ABOUT THE BUSH
SHE HAD A MAGIC

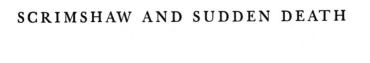

SCRIMSHAW AND SUDDEN DEATH

SCRIMSHAW AND

B

E. P. DUTTON & CO., INC

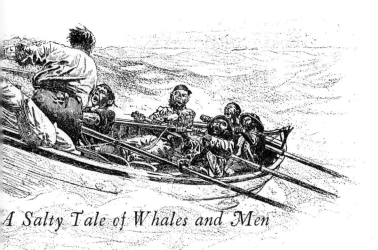

A Salty Tale of Whales and Men

SUDDEN DEATH

Brian O'Brien

Illustrated

NEW YORK ~ 1959

Library of Congress Catalog Card Number: 59-7801

For STACEY ELLEN BROWN

and DOUGLAS LEWIS BROWN

The author acknowledges his indebtedness and extends his thanks to:

Mrs. David Judson, Captain Mosher's daughter, for her kindness in loaning her father's log books;

William H. Tripp, Esq., for generously permitting the use of photographs he made during an actual whaling cruise;

Edouard Stacpole, Esq., Director of the Marine Historical Society, Mystic Seaport, Connecticut, for the use of his library and picture collection,

and to Philip F. Purrington, Esq., Curator of the Old Dartmouth Historical Society and Whaling Museum, New Bedford, Massachusetts, for his most friendly help in permitting the use of several important pictures from his collection.

*C*ontents

INTRODUCTION

THE SAGA OF America's progress would be incomplete without the logs of the old-time whalers. Before our covered wagons were crawling westward, those men in their battered barks were hauling north, south, east, *and* west, carrying the message of America into the remotest corners of the world.

They brought back light; whale oil that lit our big cities until another oil came out of the ground and killed what has been called the "exotic trade."

But the whalers did more than that. It was Captain Folger, of Nantucket, who gave Benjamin Franklin his chart of the Gulf Stream, of which no one but the whale ships had known. Matthew F. Maury's invaluable works on winds and currents came from lore collected from the humble blubber-hunters. Even the U.S. Navy went to the Pacific whalers for the formidable list of islands and shoals discovered and painstakingly charted as the greasy ships backed and filled in the endless search for sperm.

Harpoons darted in the North Atlantic and later found in whales killed in the Pacific were the evidence that sparked the exploration and discovery of the Northwest Passage.

In the Antarctic two Russian vessels, on a voyage of claim by discovery, riding out a dense fog in an icy bay, sighted, when the mist lifted, a tiny American whaleship placidly anchored between them.

With true Russian courtesy they ordered the whaleship to leave Russian territory.

"Rats!" or words to that effect, yelled the whaler captain. "We bin sheltering here for years!"

"So!" countered the wily Russian admiral. "If you know this place so well, what is its name?"

After only the slightest hesitation, Captain Nathaniel B. Palmer of Stonington, Connecticut, replied, "Palmer's Land!"

The Russians withdrew and the territory remains Palmer Land.

As our young country's early ambassadors the whalers demonstrated the American idea of freedom by clearing the eastern coast of pirates, by freeing island populations from Peruvian slavers. Whalers battled and conquered the Indonesian pirates so that trade could progress unhampered and safely in the spice ports of the Orient.

It was a whaler captain who was largely instrumental in obtaining a favorable reaction to Perry's efforts to re-open Japan's closed door.

A whaler rescued the great Irish poet and editor, James Boyle O'Reilly, from the convict camps of Western Australia.

In devotion to their concept of right forty whaleships filled their holds with rock, sailed from such ports as New Bedford, Nantucket, New London, Newport, and Gloucester, to the harbors of Savannah and Charleston, and there scuttled themselves to close the channels against blockade runners.

In their oil-soaked barks of low tonnage men were huddled together for voyages that lasted for years. Some were held in Arctic ice like the fleet of 1871: 1,200 men, women, and children escaped through pack ice by a terribly hazardous cruise in open boats.

The bark *Essex,* rammed by an enraged whale and sunk in mid-Pacific, left her crew to row and sail over 2,000 miles. Of twenty, only eight were finally rescued after a terrible ordeal of danger by hunger, thirst, storms, and cannibalism.

A few years ago a friend of the writer's died. His name was Captain Lester A. Mosher, and he was an old-time square-rigged whalemaster. He had commanded such famous vessels as the *Wanderer* and the *Canton,* and had served his life out as greenie, boat steerer, mate, and captain. For some years he served as caretaker and captain of the *Lagoda,* famous half-scale model of a whaleship in the Bourne Museum in New Bedford.

Based on his personal accounts and his logbooks, this book will present tales of the old-time whaler's life at sea and ashore: the hardships, perils, and amusements. Accounts of famous battles with the biggest mammals living, tales of fantastic courage under almost impossible privations, will attempt to explain in simple seafaring fashion why the trade of whaling, while the lowest paid and most dangerous, was the most romantic: a New England seaman had no chance with a girl unless he wore a harpooner's chock pin in his lapel.

Scrimshaw, the only American folk art apart from Indian work, was practiced on the bone and teeth of the sperm whale to while away the long waits between lowerings. During those periods fo'c'sle life was deadly boredom. But when spouts were raised and the cry, "Blo-o-ws! Blo-o-o-ws!" echoed from the masthead hoops, whalemen dropped their scrimshaw, jumped for their boats, and lowered away. Their companion during those hectic hours was sudden death!

—BRIAN O'BRIEN
Hawleyville, Connecticut

SCRIMSHAW AND SUDDEN DEATH

I.

GREASY LUCK

The excitement and danger of the hunt . . . How a maddened whale sank the Essex *. . . 2,000 terrible miles in open boats.*

"BLOWS! AH, blo-o-o-ws! Blo-o-o-ws!"

All hands tumbled out to scan the sparkling sea.

"Where away?"

Captain Shockley hobbled out of the afterhouse, dragging on his pants. He gazed upward to where the Second Mate, swinging in the foremast hoops above the belly of the topgallant sail, was hollering and pointing ahead.

"Two points off lee bow. Mile or more. Sperm, crossing our course!"

"Breaches!" screamed a hand from the main rigging.

Far away thin flashes of silver glittered in the morning sun.

"Lower away!" Captain Shockley ran for the starboard boat as the steward scrambled aloft to relieve the lookout. "Sing out at every spout!"

"Aye, aye, sir. Blo-o-ws. Blo-o-ws and white-waters!"

The deck was a bedlam of racing seamen laden with gear: harpoons, lances, boat spades. Tubs were uncovered, cranes swung in, and four boats hit water as one before the *Canton* lost way.

Our boat, being starboard, had the lead. The Captain stepped the mast, the sail bonged free, and we were heeling in to big combers while the *Canton,* luffed into the wind, rolled heavily and the lookout's cries of "blo-o-ws, blo-o-o-ws" grew fainter.

"Now!" The Captain, swinging on the great steering sweep, peered around the sail. "Bottle of rum to the first boat fast. Softly now. Gently. Strike the sail!"

The sail was taken in as quickly as set, and our oars bit water in short, powerful strokes.

"Softly!" the Captain whispered, staring past us. "Blo-o-ws! Blo-o-ws!" He was talking to himself. "Breaches! Softly my lads; he heads this way. Easy all. E-asy. Peak them oars!"

We rocked, and I heard the long sough of the spout. Then, like an island on our beam, the sperm breached, blew, and with his great flukes lifted beside us like the hand of God, he slid below.

" 'Bout ship!" the Captain whispered. "Paddles!"

We swung about and pulled like demons to catch the whale at his next rising. But he breached before we were within darting range, and, staying clear of the oily slick a whale leaves, we pulled ahead to wait for him.

"Stand by, Lester!"

I shipped my paddle, stood up, and pulled my harpoon from the bow crotch. A yard of soft iron armed with a razor-sharp toggle head and backed by six feet of rough pole was my weapon against the biggest creature on earth.

There he hung, far below us in the clear sea, a black loom that came slanting upward until I signaled the Captain to steer clear. Then the head, like a big rock, broke, water washing from it like a falling tide. The thin, slanting spout, stinking as it drifted back onto us, was unhurried. The hump slid past, scarred by squid wounds. Water cascaded off the mighty bulk like breakers from a cliff, half swamping us in the backwash.

"Give it him!"

I slammed my iron into the black streaming wall beside me, snatched the spare iron, and darted that.

"Back water!"

Both irons went up to the hitches. He felt them; the great tail flukes, eighteen feet across, rose like giant fly swatters and smashed the sea with a roaring boom, driving spray into our eyes like shot. Flukes rose again and the whale sounded.

The line whizzed through the bow chock, held there by a slender oak pin. All hands leaned outward from the yellow hemp that flaked out of the line tub and across their thwarts as our boat gathered way under the tow of the running whale.

"Change ends!" Captain called.

I skipped over the thwarts to take his place as he took mine in the bow. Now I was boat steerer and he, the whale killer.

The whale was running strong. I took turns about the loggerhead at my feet. The line groaned as we took up the slack and leaped ahead. Then the whale breached like an earthquake; his head looked mountainous. He tossed flukes and sounded again. The boat lost way as the line reached down like a gold bar into the ocean deeps. Bow oar leaned overside to test the strain, gripping the line with canvas nippers.

"How does she go?"

Seas were slopping inboard as our bow began to settle.

"Slack," he reported after a while.

"Haul away. Lively!" Captain Shockley ordered.

Early representation of the hazards of whaling

Hand over hand the line came in. Tub and Stroke fought like demons to flake it down. They knew that if the whale chose to run again, that line could snatch a man's head off.

It was a man-killing tangle amidships when the whale breached again four lengths ahead, and lay spouting heavily after his long sound.

"Close! Lay me close," the Captain whispered.

Quietly he drew his own hand lance from its beckets and slipped the leather guard from its small double-edged leaf-shaped head. Silently we drew past the terrible flukes. We were abeam of his hump, and just ahead of us his eye was less than two feet under water.

"Close!" The Captain gestured. "Wood to blackskin!"

I rode the steering sweep until we nosed in and our bow nuzzled the monster. We rocked in the wash as Captain Shockley wedged his thigh in the clumsy cleat, rested the lance against the whale, and shoved. The lance went in like a bodkin into butter, six feet of it. The Captain rode the pole, churning madly, slashing the inside with that little edged blade in the hope of reaching the whale's "life."

For a second the great mass didn't move. Then there was a mighty start. The flukes rose and slammed the sea not a foot from our stern. The lance pole snapped like a twig.

"Back water!" Shockley shouted. "He rolls!"

The great bulk almost swamped us. I saw the little sly eye and the long narrow underjaw armed with white peg teeth that slashed viciously in a welter of broken water. But we were clear, gasping, wiping spray from our eyes. Captain Shockley pulled out the spare lance and bent a short line to it.

"Again!" he said. "Closer!"

We shot down the flank of a great sea. The bilge of him rose above us. I heaved on the steering sweep until we were abaft his hump. Shockley lanced again, jerking savagely on the pole.

There was a great convulsion; the spout jetted scarlet and we ducked under the hot greasy flood.

"Spouts blood!" Tub bellowed.

The beast rolled again, flipping the lance like a wand

until its line fetched it up short and it splashed into the sea. Shockley hauled it in and yanked it straight in the gunwale crotch.

The whale was milling, spouting rapidly, thrashing the sea with flukes and fins.

"Give him line." The Captain watched every move. "Look out!"

The great animal pitchpoled, the ramlike head vertical, the terrible jaw out of water while he revolved, looking for us. But he was struck too bad. He smashed the sea to acres of foam as he went into his flurry, lying on his back, snapping that long scissor jaw, and running, towing us like a chip, while all hands held on. We could see the line wrapped about him like a slop-shop parcel as he barrel-rolled in his pain. Then there was a great burst of dark blood and he ran in a long arc until he lost way and rolled on his side.

"Fin out!" Captain Shockley said. "Ninety barrels or I'm a plum-puddiner!"

We rode beside the monster, scooping sea water to wash the blood off us; whale blood stings like acid, you know. Then we cut away the flukes and made fast to his small for the long tow back to the ship.

Well, that's how we took whales in my day. We didn't put to sea in a floating factory big as a row of houses. My uncle's bark was 120 feet long. We didn't shoot whales with three-inch cannon, neither. With us it was a yard of iron and "a dead whale or a stove boat," like the monument up in New Bedford says.

But stove boats were expected if we looked for greasy luck. There were times, though, when the whaleships themselves were attacked and stove. Like the *Ann Alexander* of New Bedford, rammed in mid-ocean by a sperm whale in 1858. And the bark *Kathleen,* sunk in 1901.

Those two were lucky, for all hands were rescued.

Not like the *Essex*.

A three-boat ship, she sailed from Nantucket on August 12, 1819, under Captain George Pollard, Jr. She was less than 100 feet long and there were twenty hands on board, signed for a cruise of indefinite duration; each man working for a lay, or share, of oil taken.

But the *Essex* was an unlucky ship from the start. She rode the Bermudas, the River Plate, the Falklands, and the Patagonia Grounds without greasing an iron. She beat around the Horn and wore up the western coast of South America, lookouts in her fore and main hoops vainly searching the heaving seas for the momentary silver flash that meant a spout.

Fifteen months from home port and she was still clean. The foremast hands were grousing, so Captain Pollard changed course and the shabby little vessel headed west, tacking and sailing along the Equator. Every dawn hoops were manned, each man taking his two-hour spell. At sundown they were recalled and the *Essex* hove to, a lonely little speck in the vast Pacific.

Then her luck turned one fine November morning.

The mate, Owen Chase, rode the mainmast hoops, sweeping the seas with his glass. Suddenly the blue of the ocean was shattered into a hundred sparkling jets. He stared like he couldn't believe his eyes. Then, "Blo-o-ws!" he yelled. "Blo-o-ws! Blows and breaches! Blo-o-ws!"

Thin brown faces peered up from the deck far below.

"Where away?" Captain Pollard shouted.

"Dead ahead. Four miles off. Pod o' sperm, sir!"

"Blo-o-ws!"

The hands could raise spouts from the deck now. They scrambled into the rigging, shading their eyes and yelling like madmen, "Blo-o-ws! White-waters!" as great black heads lifted and soused back into the sea. "Blo-o-ws!" Then, as the wide tails lifted and slid under, "There go flukes!"

"Luff!" yelled Pollard gleefully. "Hoist and swing!"

The crew rushed to their boats. Lookouts slid down back-stays, and the cabin boy clambered to take the Mate's place at masthead.

"Greasy luck at last!" shouted young Matt Joy, Second Mate. "Tubs aboard, lads!"

The boat crews tumbled their gear aboard, swung in the boat cranes, and lowered away. They dropped aboard as the *Essex* lost way, six to a boat, leaving cook and cabin boy as shipkeepers. Swiftly they stepped masts and the slim low boats heeled under lugsails, the Mate's boat ahead, the Captain's boat and Joy's fanning out to intercept the flanking whales.

"Oars!" Chase snapped. "Oars, my bullies. Spring, lads! Spring and bust your backs." He swung madly on the long steering sweep, and the boat under sail and oars sang through the sea. Then, "Blows!" he shouted. "Strike that sail!"

The mast was unshipped, the sail wrapped around it anyhow, and its foot jammed under the stern thwart.

"Paddles!" he ordered.

The men swung about on their thwarts, and ahead of them arose a mighty rocklike head, from which a slow, leisurely fore-slanting spout rose and dropped away.

"Eighty barrels!" Chase crowed. "Pull boys! Dollars in your kicks!"

The slim curved bow sliced through the combers like shears through blue silk. The whale breached again, spouted, and slid under.

"Softly!" Chase whispered. "Keep out of the slick!"

The oily wake, which no whaleman will cross for fear of

gallying the whale, glistened as they changed course to come up on his starboard side.

"Stand by!"

The harpooner shipped paddle and took his place in the bow. The whale came up from below, breached, and the oily reek filled the air. He spouted with a long sigh. The boat ranged alongside until the hump, scarred and barnacled, rose above them like a breakwater.

"Let him have it!"

The harpoon sank into the blubber. The spare iron followed, and the harpooner tossed overboard the short warps.

Then all hell broke loose.

The whale rose. His flukes lashed the sea, and a wave, caught between the whale and boat, almost swamped them.

"Stern all!" Chase gasped. "Bail!"

They backed madly as the great fan of muscle lifted above them and slammed down until the boat skidded in the wash.

"Hold fast!"

But the flukes went up again, flipping the boat like a chip. She lifted to her beam ends and fell back, her counter splintered, then jerked about and began surging through the rising seas at a great clip.

"Runnin'," the harpooner said calmly.

The boat was being dragged under as a mighty force of water raced through her started planks.

"Cut!" Chase muttered disgustedly. "He'll swamp us!"

A slash of the hatchet and they lost way. With a toss of flukes the sperm sounded. The boat began to settle.

"Calk her!" Chase ordered. "Stuff your duds into them opened seams!"

Shirts, pants, even caps, were jammed into the spaces. The *Essex* was four miles off, the other boats, out of sight.

"Pull, lads," Chase said, "while me and the harpooner

bail. Pull, you Jonahs, or we'll lose more'n a whale!"

They pulled, first with oars, then with paddles, as the boat sank under them. They were waist deep, clinging to the timbers, when the *Essex* sighted them and the cook and the boy managed to run her down to them. They hooked their boat to the falls and climbed aboard.

"Cap'n's fast," the boy reported.

The Mate made out both the Captain and Joy fast to the same running whale.

"Make for them," he ordered, jumping for the wheel. "Get them strakes patched," he ordered his crew. "We may grease an iron yet!"

The crew turned the boat over and were tacking canvas over the started planks when the cabin boy shouted, "Blows!"

"Where away?" Chase hollered. "Get that boat in the water!"

"Dead ahead, sir!" The boy's voice rose to a frightened yelp. "Headed this way, sir!"

They stared, aghast, at the great case of a sperm whale

surging above a welter of foam like the ram of a battleship. Chase spun the wheel. But before the ship could answer, the whale struck with a mighty crash just ahead of the forechain. She brought up all standing, lines snapping, masts whipping like reeds as all hands sprawled on the pitched deck. Then she lifted, and there were more crashes as top hamper carried away.

"He'll capsize us!" whimpered the boy as they felt the whale scrape along her keel.

"Pumps!" Chase fought to keep balance.

"There he blows!" muttered a hand as he jumped for the pump brake.

The whale, longer than the *Essex,* lay on the surface as though stunned.

"Hoist the recall," Chase ordered. "We'll get him yet!"

But the whale came about until they could see blood running down his head. He rolled, and his long underjaw chewed rapidly. Then he sounded until his flukes were lifted high.

"Get the boat over!" Chase shouted. "Hoist and swing!"

"Can't be did, sir," the harpooner said. "Leakin' too bad."

"Cast off the spare then. No! Hold fast!"

The whale breached close to the ship and hung there, head up, bobbing like a fishing float as he milled, his little white eyes rolling. Then his flukes slapped and he charged the ship again. They saw the wound in his forehead and a timber embedded there before he hit the strained hull again with terrible force. The fore-topmast went, the vessel listed steeply, and barrels in the hold shifted.

"Get the boat over!" Chase bellowed. "All hands! She's going!"

Slowly she began to lay over. The boat slid into the sea, followed by deck hamper, the scared seamen, and a shower of bricks from the tryworks. They scrambled into the workboat as the *Essex* fell on her beam ends and lay there, deck vertical, masts lying on the sea.

"Ahoy!"

The Captain's boat, followed by the Second Mate's, pulled toward them.

They stared at the wrecked *Essex.*

"What in God's name happened, Mr. Chase?"

"We've been stove by a whale, sir," Chase replied. "Orders, sir?"

Pollard looked a long time at the mumbling boat crews. Then, "Well. Cut the masts adrift and get her on an even keel," he said. "Then we'll see what damage she's took."

"All stove in, for'ard," Chase reported.

The hands climbed aboard mighty carefully to cut away the shrouds and stays supporting the masts. Then, as they knocked the wedges clear, the masts floated free and slowly the *Essex* swung back to an even keel. Chase stepped aboard the streaming deck.

"Can't go below, sir," he called to the Captain. "She's awash to the deck beams. We'll have to scuttle to get stores."

"We've got time," Pollard said. "Weather's clear, thank God."

They chopped holes in the deck and passed out hardtack, water, a little turtle meat, navigating instruments, a musket, and a few nails. For three days they hung close, clambering over the lurching hulk, ready to jump at every dip. They collected light spars and planks and canvas with which they raised the gunwales of the whaleboats. But a wind rose, and by noon of the third day the old ship had started to break up.

"We're a few minutes south of the Line," Captain Pollard told his crew, "and a hundred and twenty degrees west exactly. I make it fourteen hundred to the nearest land—the Marquesas," he finished.

"Cannibals!" a hand shouted. "Not me. I'll take my chances on Peru first."

"Two thousand miles to Peru," Pollard told them. "Show hands for Peru."

While he was counting the majority for Peru, the *Essex* gave a sick lurch and sank with a long moaning gurgle.

They rocked amid the ship's debris; seven in the Captain's boat, seven with Matt Joy and, since the work boat was patched and smaller, only six, including Owen Chase, weighing its gunwale to inches from the sea. They stared at each other and across the empty ocean. Two thousand miles to land! Some prayed.

"Well, men," Captain Pollard said. "There's nothing between us and kingdom come save a few half-inch planks. In my boat and Mr. Chase's boat there are compass and quadrant. So we'll lead. Mr. Joy, you'll keep in touch at all times or you'll never make a landfall. Now, give way, men, and may God have mercy on us!"

Carefully they stepped the masts, the lugsails filled, and the three boats, the longest of which was less than thirty feet, commenced a bitter voyage.

That night a squall came up. In the swirling dark the men rode their overladen boats, trying to trim them against the broken seas. At intervals they hailed each other until, just before dawn, the Captain's boat was alone on a slate-gray heaving sea.

It was the cabin boy who sighted a sail from the masthead. By noon the three boats were together again, and thankful. Then, "I'm sinking, sir," Chase reported.

The other boats drew away.

"No room aboard here," a hand in Joy's boat whispered.

The six in the leaking boat stared longingly at the others.

"We can heave her down," Chase said, "if you'll come alongside and take our cargo."

The other boats drew alongside, and the store of biscuit,

water, and gear was transshipped. Then the Mate's crew capsized their boat in the tossing sea and clung to her keel like limpets while they made shift to patch her rotted planks with tar and canvas. The sea came up as they righted her and the other boats begged them to hurry lest they all swamp. The stores were taken back, but not before much of the hardtack was soaked by the sea.

"Eat that first, before it becomes a problem," Pollard ordered.

They choked down the bitter pulp and watched jealously their thin ration of water.

For days then the sky was overcast so there could be no position taken. Squalls drove them southward, away from the direction they wanted. But they were helpless. At night they passed long lines from boat to boat.

On the eighth night there was a scream from Pollard's boat.

"Something after us!" the Captain shouted. "Stand by!"

The boats rocked in some unseen struggle. Something stank and grunted and shouldered the boats until they were crazy with fear of capsizing. All hands manned their gunwales with axes and harpoons. But when day broke, the thing was gone.

They wore on south in a swelter of heat, coiled like cats under scraps of canvas to escape the blazing sun. The wind failed, and they rowed until their hands were bloody claws. They shifted cargo, they rigged extra sails. They crawled like lost insects across the wide and empty sea. Their rations were a scrap of biscuit and a sip of water daily.

Then, by the notches in the gunwale of the Mate's boat, three weeks since the *Essex* had gone down, the overcast lifted and they sighted a low rocky island.

"Land ho!" croaked the Mate. "Give way! Pull, lads! Food and water!"

They tugged at the oars, craning sun-blistered necks, cackling breathlessly through broken lips. Then the surf took their boats, spun them helplessly, and cast them on a shelving beach about which sea birds mewed like sick cats.

Feebly they crawled up the beach, lurching as they tried to walk dry land, laughing at their weakness, cursing when the mates forced them to drag the boats to safety. Then they dropped like dead men to sleep.

When it was possible, Captain Pollard took an observation and figured they had landed on Ducie's Island. It was uninhabited and farther from Peru than they had been before they started. But no one cared. They found berries which they ate, and a few shellfish. The cabin boy knocked over a sea bird with a rock. The rest followed his example, and soon ate their fill for the first time in almost a month.

It was the following day they found the only fresh water on the island came from a spring that was covered twice a day by the sea, and scarcely gave enough for each man to quench his thirst. Then the birds grew too shy to catch, shellfish gave out, and the hands, searching for birds' eggs, explored a cave in which lay eight skeletons, side by side.

"Dead of starvation," Pollard said, "which is what'll happen to us if we stay. We'll have to put to sea again. It's but twenty-five hundred miles to Juan Fernández, Crusoe's island. Plenty of everything there."

Three refused to risk the long voyage. On December 27, five weeks after the *Essex* went down, stores were carefully divided and the three boats put off. Soon the island was out of sight. They rowed patiently, chivvied by squalls. At night they were blown apart. By day they lost precious time rowing desperately until they were again in company.

The heat increased; their water stank. Two weeks from the island Matt Joy began babbling of the green fields of Connecticut and of the cranberry pies his mother made. His crew listened in misery until he died. They rolled him into the sea and paddled hard to get away from the place where something pulled him under.

They rowed on, heaving to as squalls battered them. They spread canvas to collect rain, but it was so salt-caked that the water was unfit to drink. So they lay back, mouths open, choking and gulping the precious rain into their parched throats.

Two days after Joy's death a storm drove the boats apart again. They searched, but though Joy's boat was found, the Mate's boat was not sighted. So the two boats kept together, lonely in the wide Pacific.

The wind dropped. They crawled like skeletons over the slick doldrums, scarcely able to move the oars they had handled like sticks a couple of months before. For rest, they hunched under canvas. At night they cried in their sleep. And Captain Pollard guarded food and water with his revolver.

On January 29, 1821, a Line storm separated the two boats. Joy's little craft was never heard of again.

Pollard's boat crawled on; six sore-eyed scarecrows, stinking with dirt, their hides running with salt boils, mouths scummy and swollen so they could scarcely talk. At noon each day Pollard doled out a trickle of water and a few crumbs of biscuit. They snatched like foxes, gobbled their shares, and crawled into their holes to wait to die.

Then, one day, food and water gave out. They looked about them, at the sea lapping a few inches from the gunwales, at the empty sky, at the clean horizon. They begged for food. They said Pollard was holding out on them. They snarled like dogs and whined. And in the middle of it one of them had a fit in the bottom of the boat and died. The others looked at the dead man and scratched as they watched their captain. Another dropped, foaming, into the bilge. The three remaining snatched out sheath knives, glaring like wolves at Pollard. For a moment he raised his pistol. Then, "What else is there to do?" he said, and drew his own knife.

Bones were stripped and thrown overboard. A fire was lit on the boat's sand ballast. That night they ate.

The grisly food lasted a few days and the waiting began again. No water but rain. No food. They crouched as far as they could get from each other, their shaggy heads cocked like coyotes. And when their eyes met, they smiled.

"We loved each other as brothers all the time," Captain Pollard said afterward. "But our looks told plainly what must be done."

He watched their thin starving faces.

"We'll draw lots," he said.

He whittled slivers from the gunwale, laid them on a thwart, covered them with a blanket, and shuffled them.

"Draw!" he said.

Ramsdale, a boat steerer, drew first, the cabin boy was second. Pollard waited until the third man had taken his chance, then picked out the remaining bit of wood. Each one laid his sliver on the thwart.

" 'Tis the boy!" Ramsdale said.

Pollard reached for the lad and dragged him into the stern.

"My lad," he said. "If you don't like your lot, I'll shoot the man who touches you."

The boy, weak with starvation, laid his head on the gunwale.

"I like it well as any other," he whispered.

That night three horrible shapes crouched over the fire that sizzled in the bottom of the boat.

They were mad. They forgot the three men left on Ducie's, the boats that had vanished in the dark. They floated on, letting the varying wind fill the sail and take them where it would.

The third man died, and Ramsdale and Pollard ate until there was nothing left. Then they lay down to die.

They could not get up when they thought they heard a hail. Something jarred their boat. They wept when hands lifted them aboard the whaleship *Dauphin* of Nantucket, Captain Zimri Coffin, on February 22, three months after they had sailed away from the place where the *Essex* sank.

When they were able to talk, they told of the three men left on Ducie's Island. The following April a ship took them off, starving and off their heads with fear and loneliness.

It was almost a year before news came that Owen Chase and two men, all that remained of the six in his boat, were picked up by the British brig *Indian,* Captain William Crozier, and taken to Valparaiso, Chile. The greasy scraps found in their pockets told that they had been forced to use the same dreadful measures to survive as Captain Pollard and Charles Ramsdale.

Pollard rested a long time, far from men of the sea, then took another command, *Two Brothers,* which he lost on a Pacific reef. That finished him with blue water. He worked for a while as deck hand aboard Robert Fulton's first steamboat, the *Clermont,* a queer furtive man who kept away from his shipmates and never joined in their yarns of the sea. Though, if they'd only known it, he could have told them of suffering and privations that would have made them shiver.

II.

MY FIRST WHALING CRUISE

A greenie learns the ropes . . . Life aboard the
Canton *. . . The whaleman who became a king—*
and didn't like it!

IT'S A MIGHTY long time since I signed for my first whaling cruise aboard the *Canton* under my uncle, Captain Shockley.

I remember that even in those days a whaling captain was a grand and lordly figure who lived in a big white-painted house with fretted woodwork and a captain's walk where he could pace and watch the homing vessels through his glass.

Even the garden in my uncle's house had a seafaring look, tended, as it was, by an old whaleman, too crippled to sail any more. The walks were bordered by little white-painted stones; the gates were decorated with fancy ropework, and the beds were planted thick, as though by one who must make every inch of space useful.

The house itself was full of ancient and wonderful things; golden idols from the Orient, sandalwood boxes that scented the whole downstairs; teakwood banisters, carved tables of mother-of-pearl, and little cabinets of tiny shining things, queer-shaped and sinister, and shining weapons with edges and unexpected points that I could look at but not touch. There were carved tusks of ivory and beads of amber, scrimshaw from a hundred voyages, and a shrunken head that my mother forbade me to look at.

And my uncle was master of all this; a tall, hearty man with baked face and steady gray eyes; a slow-moving, soft-voiced man with immense dignity. I remember that though he was my uncle, I never learned his given name. To me he was Captain Shockley from start to finish.

I signed as greenie for a cruise of indefinite duration at the 170th lay. That means for every 170 barrels of oil taken, one was mine. All hands were paid by lays: the cabin boy took the long lay, 230th; boat steerers, 60th; cooper, 50th; the captain had the 10th lay. It wasn't so bad when a whaleship made port with a half-million dollars worth of oil sent home. But sometimes the ship stayed clean for an entire voyage. The 170th lay of nothing isn't much!

I boarded the bark one Sunday morning to the music of church bells from New Bedford and Fairhaven and the wheeze of concertinas from the waterfront barflies come to tell the crew good-by. I was ashamed to have my people see me off, like a kid going to school. But as the paddle tug cast us off out by No Man's Land and started back to port with the wives and sweethearts waving their handkerchiefs and wishing us greasy luck, I felt sort of forlorn in a ship that seemed suddenly mighty small for all the gear, animals, and people aboard her.

The *Canton* was 239 tons and about the size of a Pullman car. Aboard were 6 pigs, 2 in the family way; 20 chickens; and 36 crew: the Captain, 4 mates, 4 boat steerers, cooper, blacksmith, cook, steward, 16 able seamen, 5 greenies like me, steerage boy, and cabin boy. That wasn't all; there were

The bark CANTON

four 28-foot whaleboats on the cranes and two spares on the gallows over the afterdeck. Below were casks for water and oil, stores, trade goods for barter, spare canvas, hardware, copperware, crockery, provisions, sundries, and slop-chest supplies; between 650 and 700 different items.

The crew had to learn to move amidst all this gear without stepping on each other and to catch the biggest animals in the world to boot. Those who were able were setting sail under the shouts of the Mate. Some lay drunk in the scuppers, some sang, some sniveled. It didn't look like any picnic!

I caught my uncle's eye, and he looked through me like I was a stranger. From then on he never called me anything but "here, you!" I guess he didn't want to show favor to a relative.

I didn't know where to go or what to do. But I figured the less questions I asked, the less trouble I'd get into. So I followed some foremast hands down the fo'c'sle scuttle into the gloom and stink of what was to be my home for a couple of years, I thought. It creaked, and water dripped through the walls. Streaks of grimy light came from deadlights set in the deck over us, and a fog surrounded the smoky glow from a whale-oil lamp swinging from a beam. The triangular space was lined with white-limed bunks littered with gear. Chests, coats, bottles broken and unbroken slid about the deck as the ship butted her heavy bows into the rising sea. The fo'c'sle smelled of tar, sweat, liquor, disinfectant, bilge, and the ancient, musty rancidity of whale blubber. I was stowing my sea bag in one of the lower bunks near the eyes of the ship when a seamy-faced seaman with the eyes of a circus clown took a bottle from his mouth and shook his head. I lifted my sea bag out of the dark, moist space. He jerked his head toward an upper bunk to the side of the deck ladder.

"Drown yerself in that for'ard bunk, sonny," he said. "Always take an upper if ye can. Never know what'll fall on ye if you sleep in a deck bunk. Greenie?"

I told him I was.

"Name of Jimmy Owen," he said. "Able Seaman. I bin boat steerer, header, master of my own ship, once." He patted his bottle fondly. "Ruined by drink. Take warnin', young fellow. Here!" He flipped a long cotton bag to me. "Donkey's breakfast aft. Don't fill her too tight; she's all you'll have to sleep on for a year or so."

I figured what he meant and fumbled through the larboard alley to where an opened bale of straw offered filling for the cotton mattress Owen had given me. I got it back and into my berth.

"Where do we get drinking water?" I asked Owen, who was finishing his bottle.

"Ye won't like it," he mumbled. "But come along."

On deck he pointed to the mainmasthead, where a tiny hook pot was made fast.

"Up there; get that thief and help yerself from the scuttle by the afterhouse. Then ye return the thief to masthead. That way ye won't waste water." He winked. "Serves ye right for drinkin' the stuff."

I was stuck. I'd rather have taken a beating than climb that swaying mast. But Owen was watching me with an old-fashioned look in his eye, and I knew I had to go. I got into the shrouds and worked my way up the ratlines like a crab up a slick stairway. At the mainyard I felt as though the mast was falling over on me. I crawled through the lubber's hole and reached the topgallant, and there I hung, eyes tight shut, sick as a dog, while the mast swung back and forth in long dizzy arcs. At every swing I thought the tail of my shirt was in the sea. I didn't want water then; all I wanted was dry land and lots of it. But I heard the clank of the thief up there and I had to get it. I think I left my fingerprints in the timber of that topgallant mast, I gripped her so tight. I snatched the thief and tucked it in my shirt. Then I had to get down. Step by step I managed it past bellying sails, creaking yards, and tar-sticky sheets. But when I reached the scuttle and shoved the thief in its bunghole, I was dry as the galley smoke pipe.

"Hand her over, sonny," Owen said when I'd finished gulping.

I gave him the thief and watched him drink a very little.

"Last man takes her up," he said, and went up those rat-lines like a monkey.

That wasn't the last of the kind things Jimmy Owen did for me. I guess he knew as well as I did that I could never have made that awful climb just then. But I learned, and in a few days I could beat most of the crew to masthead.

We greenies had it fairly easy that day; all work was done by the able seamen. But just before sundown the Mate called all hands.

We crowded about the mainmast, those who could walk, hanging on to standing gear, jamming ourselves against the brick tryworks, for the *Canton* was rolling and pitching like a hog on ice. The Captain balanced himself on the main-scuttle and looked us over like a drill sergeant. Around him the mates stood.

He told us that we were signed on for a long and, he hoped, greasy voyage. We were to remember who was boss aboard the *Canton,* to obey orders without question and to keep one hand for ourselves and one for the ship at all times. He gave us greenies a week to box the compass, reef, steer, and know the ropes. "Or," he roared, "no watch below until you do." There'd be plenty of food, we were told; the after-guard ate the same as the fo'c'sle, so there must be no grumbling. And no waste. Anyone caught wasting food would go on bread and water for a week. Tobacco and comforts could be had through the steward from the slop chest and the price charged against our lays. That was all. He then told the mates to pick their watches.

We were divided between the First and Second mates. I was under Mr. Reynolds, Second Mate; larboard watch.

I soon learned the ropes and began to understand something of the order of a whaleship. The Captain had his cabin across the stern, his stateroom and privy to starboard.

For'ard of him the mates had their cabins and messroom with the cook and steward. Amidships, where the boat steerers, cooper, blacksmith, and boys slept in bunks you could scarcely stuff a dead man into, was called the steerage. In the wet, dark triangular fo'c'sle, its deck cluttered with sea chests, oilskins, clothing, bits and pieces of calico swinging from stanchions, lived twenty-one foremast hands.

We had little time to worry about hard lying. The *Canton* was sailing due south, Owen told me, and we were jumping to have all shipshape before we raised whales.

First we fitted the boats; each one a sweet-run twenty-eight-foot clinker-built double-ender, sharp as a chisel at bow and stern and six feet wide amidships. The gunwale in the middle was twenty-two inches from the keel, rising to thirty-seven inches at bow and stern. That gave the boat buoyancy to ride her dry over waves that would swamp any ordinary craft. Gunwale and keel were heavy timbers, but the planking was only half-inch white cedar. The bow thwart had a three-inch hole for the mast, and in the stern box was the loggerhead, a stout round timber for snubbing and controlling the line. Four feet of the bow was boxed in and backed by a stout plank with a half-round notch called the clumsy cleat. The harpooner braced his knee in that notch when darting his iron. Opposite every thwart were holes for the rowlocks which were muffled by greased yarn to keep the oars silent when stealing up on to a whale.

The crew was six men. The boat header—the captain or a mate—in the stern, steering with a 22 foot sweep. Then came stroke oar, or after oar, with a 16 foot blade; tub oar, 17 feet; midship oar, 18 feet; bow oar, 17 feet; and harpooner's oar, 16 feet. The reason for the different lengths (the harpooner only pulled when going after a whale) was to balance the vessel. But rowing wasn't all. The harpooner,

who was better known as boat steerer (because after the
boat was fast to the whale, he changed ends with the mate,
whose job it was to kill the whale), had also to strike the
whale and help manage the mast and sail. Bow oar helped
in setting and taking in the mast. Midship oar, having the
longest and heaviest oar, did nothing but pull. Tub oar had
also to take care of the line in the tubs, and Stroke oar, or
After oar, bailed, helped with mast and sail. The boat header
steered, commanded the boat, and decided how best to kill
the whale.

In addition to six men and six massive oars, each boat
carried five paddles, a mast and sail, water keg, candles,
lantern, compass, first-aid box, hardtack, hatchet and knife
for cutting the line, waif, flags on poles, fire-making ma-
terials, bailer, and two great line tubs containing six hundred
yards of the finest Manila hemp. And that's not all. There
were two live irons (harpoons ready for use); razor-sharp
toggle heads on three-foot iron shafts mounted on six-foot
rough hickory poles; two or three spare irons secured to the
sides above the thwarts; two or three lances (wicked little
spoon-shaped heads with cutting edges on five-foot shafts);
six-foot poles; and a chisel-edged fluke spade on a pole that
was used for chopping off the whale's tail and for cutting
holes to hold the line by which we would tow him back to
the ship. All those blades had to be guarded with wooden
sheaths made fast with yarn to the thwarts.

What with all that gear and the six-man crew, the boat—
which could be lifted by two strong men—carried 2,500
pounds. The Yankee whaleboat was and still is known all
over the world as the finest water craft ever built. Those
five great oars could drive her through the sea at ten miles
an hour.

We went over them like mother monkeys, smoothing,

painting all but the pine platforms at bow and stern where the boat steerer and boat header stood. They were left rough for safe footing.

The most important whaling gear was the line: Manila hemp, about three-quarters of an inch through, three-strand, and half as strong again as ordinary rope of the same size. Its breaking point was three tons dead weight. We had to coil it down in left-hand flakes so it would run out of the tub smoothly; a whale line kinking under the tow of a running whale can twitch a man's leg off, Owen told me. Later I saw it done. We ran the line to the yards and let it tow astern to straighten and moisten and stretch it. Then we coiled it down and drew it out and coiled it again while the mates, who would be responsible for it, went over every inch of line in each tub.

We jumped to help the lordly boat steerers mount their irons on six-foot rough bark poles. We turned the grindstone while the mates put razor edges on the tiny leaf-shaped lance heads that would find the "life" of the great whales.

Then, one fine morning, the mates began picking their boat crews. We stood to, Mate's watch to starboard, Second Mate's watch to larboard, while the mates and boat steerers walked up and down under the Captain's eye, felt our muscles, thumped our chests, and asked about our experience. We greenies stood at the ends of the lines and tried not to look anxious. I was pretty husky, and maybe Owen, who was respected by all hands, put in a word for me. Mr. Nanton, the Mate, picked me for his boat, and I was proud enough to bust.

"You'll pull after oar," Mr. Nanton told me. "You'll help handle the line when it comes in, and you'll watch the logger-head."

Boat steerer, or harpooner, was George Leeds, a small

man, bald as a fish but with a torpedo beard and a big white mustache. Religious, he was, but it didn't show when he was fast to a whale. Bow oar was pulled by Pete Brava; midship oar was like a feather when big Olaf handled it. Owen had tub oar and managed the line.

I didn't have much time to blow because I was the only greenie in a boat crew. Owen kept after me like a jailer, making me learn the place of everything in that boat until I could have snatched anything he told me in the middle of the night. Then the Mate drilled us. It was hoist and swing from dawn to dark all across the Gulf Stream. Mate would whistle and we'd drop whatever we were doing, heave the tubs aboard, kick in the cranes that support the boat under its big wooden davits, lower and slide down the falls to our places in a boat half swamped by the *Canton's* way. Rocking, we'd swoop down the big combers, the Mate yelling like an Indian, out oars and be pulling, one—two—one—two, until our craft creamed through the seas like a dolphin. Then Leeds would take his place in the bow, wedge his thigh in the clumsy cleat—to give him leverage—and dart his iron. Man, he could heave that harpoon like a spear, and hit a harness keg two boat lengths off! Then he'd change ends with the Mate and we'd go through all the motions of fastening to a whale, running in close, and killing him. After that, it was "pull and spring your backs out!" to the ship.

We did this until our boat crew was like a machine. Every man knew his place and just what he had to do under all straits. We could have taken our boat by sail, oars, or paddles right down a whale's throat.

By this time we were standing lookout watch in the hoops at fore and mainmast heads. The hoops were iron rings bolted in pairs above the topgallant yards. Every morning at sunup the hoops were manned; the lookouts were relieved every two hours until dark, when they were called down. I thought I had my sea legs. But swinging in the hoops, a hundred feet above the deck, taught me different. Every time the *Canton* rolled, the masts bent like fishing rods, with the lookouts the plugs. When they swung back, we left our insides ten fathoms below us. Centrifugal force, an engineering fellow told me once. But seasick or no seasick, we stood our tricks in the hoops. When I got used to it, it was sort of grand. Up there far above the greasy deck, cut off from all below by the belly of the topgallant sail, with nothing about me but the blue sky, gave me time to think. I'd cling there, my only footing two narrow planks called crosstrees, my arms over the ring and a glass about my neck, watching, with George Leeds, for the tiny flash of silver that meant a whale spouting.

All through the day silence was kept aboard the *Canton*, for noise might prevent the deck from hearing the lookout's hail. It wasn't until the order "Alow from aloft!" at sundown that loud talk, singing, and Pete Brava's accordion were permitted. That was in the fo'c'sle. The boat steerers had their own place; the workbench by the tryworks, the brick erection abaft the foremast that held the great boilers for cooking oil out of the blubber.

Farther aft by the mainmast the gallows, supporting the two spare boats and sundry gear, sheltered the cabin skylight, and, on the larboard side, the cooper's chest and grindstone. To starboard was the blacksmith's bench. In the stern was the afterhouse, sheltering the wheel, on the starboard side, the galley, and opposite the captain's companion.

Rolling southeast in the warm nights, with seasickness and the awkwardness of a strange ship all behind, made me glad I'd come to sea. The *Canton* rolled gently, her cordage slatting in the light breeze, upperworks creaking rhythmi-

"Ah blows"—whale sighted

Ready to lower

Lowering for whales

Down for whales

cally. Aft the binnacle and cabin skylight lit up the bearded face of the helmsman. Amidships, boat steerers and mates talked softly, the red glow of their pipes brightening and fading. For'ard we foremast hands made ourselves comfortable against the winch and knightheads, listening to Pete Brava. Some of the greenies were still puzzling over the knots and splices they'd learned. Others just lay there, smoking their precious tobacco. Jimmy Owen was sewing an old pair of red flannel underdrawers inside a tattered pair of trousers.

"Both so holey they ain't no good, one without the other," he grunted, "so I sews them together in hopes the holes don't come opposite. And don't split your face smirkin', sonny. You'll be wearin' patches on patches and a patch over all before this cruise is done."

I wasn't worried; most of us were barefoot, in thin rags of shirt and cotton slop-chest pants.

"Where we bound for?" one of the Second Mate's boat crew wanted to know. "Anyone heard anything?"

"Wherever there's whales," George Leeds said. "We'm just about off the Bermuda Grounds. Maybe we'll try the Westerns, in the Azores, then bear south to the Saint Helena or the Carrolls, down along the African Coast, or the Crozets off Cape Town."

"What are *grounds?*" I asked.

"Places where the whales meet to feed," Owen told me. "Whales are steady-going beasts, always come back to the same grounds after their passaging 'til they get killed out. My guess is that we try Off the River, that's South Atlantic, or the Desolations, even the Off Shore Grounds or the South Pacific."

"That's for me," one of the greenies put in. He was a

thin-faced townie from New York State, called Nelson; always blowing about how clever he was.

"We gets in the South Seas, I'll jump this tub and get me a job as king of one of them cannibal islands."

"One thing," Leeds said. "You ain't got enough meat on you to make 'em a meal. And if I catches you spittin' to windward again, I'll fetch you a clip on the ear."

"I knew a fellow once who was king of an island," Owen said, "and he was mighty glad to get away from it."

"Musta been off his head," Nelson jeered.

"Stow yer gab and listen," one of his mates said.

Owen got his pipe going comfortably and began. . . .

Jim Brown, his name was, pulled bow oar in the mate's boat of the old *Lady Jane*. She was eighteen months from home port and had taken less than eighty barrels of oil. She'd searched the Off Shore Grounds, reaching and running before the wind all along the Line without raising a spout. They hadn't touched land for over six months: the water was ropy and the hardtack, full of weevils. The foremast hands were sojering and talking back to the mates, and one of them said he was coming down with scurvy. The Captain was against putting in at one of the islands for fear his crew would desert. They headed southeast, but the hands made such a fuss, he agreed to anchor off a tiny lonesome island for water, fruit, and maybe a turtle or so.

Soon as the anchor held outside a reef, the crew started lowering like the sea was full of whales. So the Captain, mates, and boat steerers drove them back with guns and blackjacks, forced them to weigh anchor, and battened them all in the fo'c'sle.

That island being so close was too much for Jimmy Brown. Soon as the boat steerers started getting sail on her, he slipped overside and started swimming. No one saw him go; the afterguard was too busy wearing the ship around, and by the time he reached the reef, the *Lady Jane*—poor, battered old tub with weed a fathom long dripping from her bilge and her patched sails slatting—was headed for the open sea.

Jim crawled on to the coral, scraping his hands and knees raw, and managed to get his footing in the breaking seas. The beach was three hundred yards off. But in the clear green water he saw half a dozen long blue sharks. Jim felt mighty uneasy; he had forgotten all about sharks. He stood up and started yelling. But the ship was too far off to hear him and there was no sign of life on the beach. He looked along the reef, but most of it was a couple of feet under water. He was wondering what to do when a wave washed him into the lagoon. He was almost choked himself, getting back to footing. But another big comber was gathering above him like a green glass wall.

He said what prayers he could remember and let the big wave carry him toward the shore. The sea went on and left him swimming as hard as he could, his eyes straining for a sight of those sharks. Seas passed under him and shut off the line of beach. Others lifted him so he seemed to be looking down at it. He turned on his side to get some breath and there, not two boat lengths away, was the back fin of a shark. He started splashing and shouting to scare the beast off. Then he saw another on his starboard side. He was tiring but he had to keep splashing. Every stroke he drew his legs under him, scared to death that those horrible teeth would rip him to bits. Then a wave lifted him and showed him a crowd of people on the beach. They were painted and wore feathers and carried clubs and spears.

Cannibals, for sure, he figured. But it was better to be speared or clubbed to death than eaten alive by those sharks.

So Jimmy kept swimming until a big breaker threw him, rolling over and over, up the steep beach. He scrambled as far as he could from the water and got to his feet, swaying with tiredness and coughing water out of his lungs. Then the people started for him, shouting and waving their spears, pointing to him and to the sea. He got himself set to grab one of those spears and make a fight for it. But the people dropped down on their hands and knees and started patting the sand about his feet.

"What's the idea?" he said.

He remembered yarns of seamen cast ashore and being taken for spirits. Maybe they'd never seen a white man before. He was waiting for the next move when a conch shell trumpet began to moan and an old man came out of the trees beyond the beach. He wore a helmet made of a dried blowfish and a red-and-black bark cloth hanging from his shoulder. A necklace of shark teeth dangled on his tattooed ribby chest, and he carried a long staff with a carved wooden shark at one end. Behind him came a crowd of girls in leaf skirts with flowers in their hair and necklaces of red seeds. They crowded close to Jimmy, making cooing sounds. Then they crouched down, staring at him. All but one. She was the fattest girl Jimmy had ever seen. She was oiled from head to foot and her hair was stuck full of little pink flowers. She kept grinning at Jimmy and jabbering to the old man. The old man took a wreath of flowers from the fat girl and put it around Jimmy's neck. Then the other girls got up and put flowers on him and danced around, shouting.

"Look," he said; now he was sure they weren't going to hurt him. "How about some grub. *Kai-kai*. Savvy?" He pointed to his mouth and made eating motions.

The old man took his hand and led him back through the trees to a village under a tall cliff that was screened from the sea by bush. There were steep roofed huts of bark and palm thatch, little sheds with canoes in them, and a shelter with a fire burning in it. Behind the fire was a wall with dried shark jaws hanging from it, and several logs carved to look like sharks.

By this time Jimmy was beginning to realize what was happening. These people were shark worshipers, and seeing him swim in from the ocean and those sharks not touching him, they figured he was a stronger spirit than their shark god. So he walked under the shelter and sat down on a log by the fire.

There were about sixty people in the village—men, women, and a dozen little kids. He made signs again that he wanted food. Three girls ran off and came back with a big carved wooden bowl of kava. That's a drink made of coconut milk and certain pepper leaves. Jimmy had tasted it before, and found it made him drowsy and mighty comfortable. What he didn't know was that the girls made it by chewing the leaves and spitting them into the bowl, pouring in the coconut milk and stirring it with their hands until it turned a brownish-green. Anyway, he took a good pull and felt better. He handed the bowl to the old man, who took a swallow and passed it to the fat girl, and she had some. That meant she was next important to the old man, who was evidently the chief. One of the girls brought little raw fish on a plantain leaf and some red bananas. The fat one slapped her, took the food, and handed it to Jimmy with a smile he didn't like at all. But he ate the food and then signed them to go away while he thought things over. They got up, and some of the girls put up a sort of mat fence around the shelter. Others brought in soft grass mats and signed Jimmy to lie down on them. He did so, and they stared at him until he began to feel embarrassed that he had no shirt on. Then one of the girls came forward and tried to take his pants off.

"Belay that!" Jimmy yelled, holding on to his belt.

The fat one chased the others out and then *she* tried to take his pants off.

"Go away!" Jimmy shouted. "Ain't you got no modesty? Go on. Beat it!"

The chief came in, said something, and the fat girl went out, looking back and smiling, coy-like.

"She want look-see you white-skin all over," the chief said.

"No reason to drag a man's pants off," Jimmy growled. "Hey, you savvy American-talk."

"Me, Raratonga-boy. Savvy work Portugee-ship. Take boat, jump ship. Come along this place long time altogether. This place man think me spirit. All same this place man think you spirit. You-me big man for this place."

"Who's that fat lump?" Jimmy asked. "Big fat woman?"

"When I come, I marry Mary this place. Pletty soon catch pickaninny. Pickaninny name Mani."

"Your daughter, eh? Well, tell her to keep away from me."

"More better you marry Mani," the chief said. "Mani like you plenty."

"Nothing doing," Jimmy howled. "I'm not ready to get married for years."

"More better you marry. S'pose Mani tell people you no god, they savvy *kai-kai* you."

"You're an old fraud," Jimmy snapped. "I won't do it."

But there was a nasty look in the chief's bloodshot eyes.

"Wait a bit," Jimmy begged. "Give me time to get settled-like. We'll talk about it later."

The old man left him, and Jimmy got some sleep. Next day he walked in the village and all hands followed him, clapping their hands and giving him bananas and things. Whatever he pointed at, he got. There was roast pig; he let them know he liked cooked fish better than raw. They brought sweet limes and coconut milk for him to drink. But none of them would stay around and talk to him; he figured that Mani had put a taboo on him.

One night he got away and climbed the cliff. Mani followed and caught up with him just as he got a good signal fire going. She carried on something awful, and the chief said he had to marry her right away.

"You no marry, man *kai-kai* you one-time," the chief threatened.

There was nothing for it but to agree. She yelled like a steam whistle, picked Jimmy up in her arms, and started rubbing noses with him.

"Let me down!" he hollered.

But she dragged him in to the village and started a feast going right away. There was roast pig and fish, taro, yams, little raw shellfish, coconuts, and bananas cooked every which way. The pretty girls danced and the old men banged drums and blew on conches until Jimmy was half deaf. And Mani sat beside him, feeding him bits of fish with her fat fingers until he was crazy with temper. So he got at the kava bowl and kept at it until he fell over. When he woke up next morning, Mani was sharing his special shelter.

From then on, he was miserable. She'd let no one near him, even with food, and everywhere he went, she followed. She had a taboo on him so that he could get nothing to eat or drink except from her. And that went on for three years.

Then the chief died. There was another big feast and the body was buried at the top of the cliff among the biggest collection of skulls Jimmy had ever seen. And all the people bowed down to him and gave him the shark-head staff to carry. He was king now, Mani told him, and she was queen.

But all Jimmy Brown wanted was to get away from that island. Every chance he got, he climbed the cliff, but he never sighted a sail. Until one morning he sneaked off while she was sleeping. It was a beautiful day, the sky blue as heaven except for the white cloud that always hung over the island. The surf was booming and the palms whispering in the light wind. He was just enjoying the blessedness of being alone when he rounded a rock and there was Mani staring out to sea. Jimmy was about to duck back out of sight when he saw what she was looking at.

"Sail ho!" he yelled. "There's a ship. Sail ho!"

She ran at him and fetched him a clump on the head that knocked him flat. Next thing he knew, he was lying in the bushes with Mani beside him, watching the ship drop anchor and a whaleboat put off with two casks in tow.

"White fellow prenty," she said.

"Sure. They come for water and food."

Conches were blowing, and down the beach the island people were gathering with spears and clubs. The boat lay to inside the reef while the people aboard studied the situation.

"Tell people hide spears," Jimmy said. "White fellows friends." He got up and ran down the beach. "Boat ahoy! Come ashore. These are friendly!"

Mani was shouting to the islanders to put down their weapons. The whaleboat came in close. There were five men at the oars and an officer in the stern.

"Bark, *Kathleen,*" the officer called. "Who be you? Castaway?"

"Come ashore." Jimmy yelled. "We got fruit and meat and everything."

The men landed and gathered around, shaking his hand and telling their names.

"I'm the Mate," the officer said. "Tell them people to give us water."

The whalemen went up the beach, followed by all the pretty girls. It wasn't long before they looked mighty friendly. All day they worked, filling water casks and loading fruit and yams and three pigs. By nightfall there were twenty whalemen on shore handing out trade goods: calico, fishhooks and tobacco and oil to pay for the food. Big fires were lighted and the girls were handing round bowls of kava while a feast cooked in a big trench full of hot rocks and covered with leaves.

"Nice little lay you got for yourself," the Mate said. "All these people bowin' down to you."

"Look, Mister Mate," Jimmy whispered. "I want off this island. I'm a good whaleman. I bin here upward of four years. I'm a good whaleman, Mister. Take me off."

"What will you pay for your passage?" the Mate asked, looking him over.

"I ain't got anything."

"You been here four years and you ain't got a packet of pearls hid out someplace?"

"No, I haven't."

"Then you don't deserve to leave."

"I got you food and water, Mister. They might have killed you."

"No pearls, no passage," the Mate said. "Gimme some of that kava."

The whalemen were dancing with the girls to a concertina, and some of them looked a bit the worse for the kava. Jimmy looked around and noticed that the men of the village were gone. He excused himself and went through the trees to the village. The men were there collecting clubs and spears. Mani grabbed him.

"People savvy white fellow all same you," she whispered. "Savvy you no god. More better we *kai-kai* white fellow."

"No," Jimmy said.

"If white fellow go, people savvy *kai-kai* you, me. Better we *kai-kai* white fellow. Then you god sure."

There was a wicked look on her fat face, and Jimmy knew she meant every word she said. They were waiting for the kava to make the whalemen sleepy, then they'd rush them. Jimmy had a feeling he'd be killed with the rest.

"Wait," he whispered. "I make talk with white fellow. When all sleep, I call you."

He ran off into the darkness. Most of the whalemen were half seas over.

"Got them pearls?" The Mate grinned.

"Look, Mister," Jimmy whispered. "They're getting ready to rush you. Look at your boats. Not a guard on them. Get going, Mister."

"Don't gammon me, boy," the Mate sneered.

"Look about you. No men. See? And look at them girls; they're scared half to death. There's spears back in the village."

The Mate sobered up, quick.

"Ahoy, men," he said softly. "Town-ho! Get the girls and walk along the beach to the boats. Softly now, and when I give the word, run."

One by one the men shook each other and got up, dragging the girls with them, and started toward the boats, pretending to sing as they went. At the last second they pushed the girls away and shoved off, the Mate counting as they tumbled aboard three boats. Jimmy jumped into the Mate's boat as Mani and the islanders came screeching along the beach.

"Starn all!" the Mate yelled. "Give way!"

He dragged a musket from under the gunwale as the boats smashed through the walls of surf. A few spears splashed around them and then they were away, the islanders howling in the darkness behind them. They weathered the reef and the lights of the bark *Kathleen* were close aboard.

The Captain watched them secure the boats.

"Trouble?" he asked. "All hands safe?"

"And one extra," the Mate said. "This one says he's king of the island. Says he wants passage home."

"I'm a good whaleman, sir," Jimmy pleaded. "Rowed bow oar, I did, for the *Lady Jane*. I'll do anything, sir. But take me home."

"You'll sign foremast hand at a hundred and twentieth lay," the Captain said. "Get for'ard."

"Yes, sir," Jimmy said. "Thank you, sir."

It was thirteen months before the *Kathleen* made home port, and Jimmy Brown wouldn't go ashore at any place she touched. Last I heard of him, he was back in Ohio; said he wanted to get as far as he could from the sea. He had himself a tidy chicken farm. So maybe he'd tucked away a few pearls after all.

"Now you want to be a cannibal king, sonny?" Leeds chuckled.

"Gwan," Nelson jeered. "I don't believe a word of it. How come you know so much about it, pal?"

"I was mate of the *Kathleen*," Owen said quietly.

III.

THERE HE BLOWS!

Fast to a whale . . . Stove boat in a shark-infested sea . . . Rescue . . . Why a whale could not have swallowed Jonah.

ONE MORNING, due east of Bermuda, the Captain ordered casks up from the 'tween decks. Dad Smith, the cooper, slopped a little sea water in them and ladled boiling oil on top of it. Then he headed up the casks.

"Oil boils the water," Leeds explained to me, "and the steam and hot oil seals the casks so they won't leak." He cocked his beard and squinted around the horizon. "Masthead, sonny. I smell whales."

We took our places in the foremast hoops. I sniffed the cool air and thought I smelled something, but it could have been the hot oil the cooper was using.

"Keep yer eyes open," Leeds warned me. "Five pound of tobacco for the first to raise spouts, remember."

In the main hoops the Third Mate and his boat steerer scanned the sea. There was a look of excitement about them, as though they too could smell whales.

It was a grand morning. Under our feet the sail bellied

out, hiding all but the end of the bowsprit. Ropes creaked about us, and the wind lifted my shaggy hair. Leeds, pipe sagging from the yellow middle of his mustache, was sweeping the horizon with his glass. He froze. Then drove his elbow into my ribs and bawled right in my ear, "Blo-o-ws! Blooooooows! Thar she blooooows!"

"Blo-o-ws!" yelled the Third Mate.

I caught the flash of silver; a tiny reflection on the sea that repeated itself.

"Blo-o-ws!" I screamed. First time in my life I'd ever seen a whale spout. "Blo-o-o-o-o-ws! There she——" In my excitement I slipped off the yard.

"Hup there!" Leeds grabbed me by the arm just in time and yanked me back.

"Where away?" Captain Shockley bawled from the deck.

"Dead ahead," Leeds called. "Crossing to starboard. Sperm! Blo-o-o-ws! All over the ocean!"

I could see the flash of spouts like the sea was dusted with bird shot. The Third Mate and his boat steerer were already sliding down the main backstay.

"Breaches," Leeds bellowed as a black shape appeared and vanished in a patch of white foam. "Git below, sonny!"

How we reached the deck without killing ourselves, I'll never know. The cabin boy and a greenie shinnied up the foot ropes to relieve us.

"Blo-o-ws!" squeaked the boy before he even reached the foreyard.

The deck was a hurrah's nest of tubs, spades, line, and yelling seamen.

"Hoist and swing!" the mates roared.

All four boats were lowering: Captain's on the starboard side and the three mates' boats to larboard. I helped Leeds heave the two tubs aboard our boat while Jimmy Owen kicked in the cranes. The boat hit water as the bark luffed. We slid down the falls, tumbled into our places, and shoved off.

The stern of the *Canton* swung right over us. But a heave of the steering sweep shot us under her counter and we were away to leeward, the three other boats wide on our beams.

"Give way," the Mate said softly. "Not a word out of ye now. Pull and save yer breath for countin' your money. First strike for us and it's greasy all the way. Spring, my bullies! Break your backs, my lucky lads!"

I braced my foot against the loggerhead and pulled until my oar bent like a willow. The Mate stood above me, peering over our heads and talking a blue streak. I snatched a quick look abeam. We were gaining on the other boats.

"Pull, you stringy-backed worms!" the Mate growled. "We ain't anchored!"

The seas were marching past as we surged through them. The *Canton* seemed far astern of us already.

"My Sam!" the Mate said suddenly.

I turned to see what was afoot. And got a clout from the Mate's knuckles that nearly stove my head in.

"How many times I gotta tell you to keep yer eyes in the boat?" he snapped. "You watch me! I'll tell you when to see the sights!"

I pulled, blinking water out of my eyes.

"Peak oars," the Mate said. "Turn about and paddle!"

We must have looked like a beetle on his back with the five long oars sticking out of us. I spun on my thwart, snatched a paddle from under the gunwale and——

"Breaches!" Leeds called from the bow.

Ahead a line of heads lifted like tide rocks, the sea rolling back from them. They came at us like a row of elephants, thin spouts slanting forward from their high square snouts, shoving great billows of foam ahead of them. Then the heads went under, and I caught a glimpse of mighty flat black flukes.

"Way 'nough," the Mate snapped. "Stand by, George!"

Leeds shipped his paddle, stood up, and drew his number one iron from its crotch beside him. I don't know when he had done it. But Jimmy Owen, next to me, had rove his line from tub around the loggerhead over the thwarts along the trough made by our peaked oars, under the kicking strap, through the chock to the iron Leeds held. In the bow crotch lay another iron, the spare, looped to the line by a short warp.

Leeds squinted about him, set himself, and waited.

Whales breached on both sides of us. We rocked wildly in the cross seas kicked up by their enormous bodies. The boat swung in toward the sperm bull to our starboard side.

"Give it to him!" the Mate snapped.

The side of that whale lifted like the sheer of a battleship right alongside. Water poured off him, and he stank. Leeds poised his iron, and I saw it sink to the hitches in that black hide. At once Leeds snatched the spare iron and darted that beside the first.

The whale rolled a little, and a sea slopped aboard to fill us to the gunwales.

"Back!" the Mate said softly. "Back, all hands. Get her about. He's sounding!"

The flukes rose lazily right beside us, lifted until they looked like a roof. Then they slammed down, and we gasped for breath in the driven spray. He wrenched us about and we rocked wildly, almost awash in the broken seas.

"Bail!" Leeds shouted from the bow. "Can't see a blasted thing!"

I kicked water out of her and managed to keep clear of

the line that was looping out of the tub and across the thwarts between us. Somewhere ahead the whale breached. The Mate bent over, snatched the line, and threw another turn about the loggerhead beside my foot. Then we jerked ahead, slapping through the seas, the line taut as a fiddle string.

"Change ends," the Mate called.

We were plunging and rocking, the line was twanging like a banjo between us. But the Mate danced forward over the thwarts while Leeds balanced on his way aft; they held on to each other amidships, passed, and fell into their new places in the bow and stern.

Up to this time I hadn't had a chance to think much; been too heart-in-my-mouth excited, I guess. But I took a look around. The *Canton* was hull down, maybe a couple of miles away. I could see none of the other boats. And there we were, towing along at the rate of knots, a thousand miles from land, astern of a sperm whale that could come about and mash us into pudding any time he felt like it.

His flukes rose some two boat lengths away, and he slid under, leaving a long patch of oily water.

"His slick," Jimmy Owen said, slopping water on the line. "Cross that and he'll get gallied. Kind of acts like a telegraph to him."

"Cast off," the Mate called from the bow. "Sounding deep."

We had almost lost way, but the line was still stiff as a bar. Leeds threw the turn off the loggerhead and the line smoked out through the chock. Regular as clockwork the flakes flipped out of the tub and across the thwarts, one after another, until Owen made fast the line from the spare tub. That went, too, straight down into the ocean, the seas breaking over us now we were anchored.

"How's the line?" Mate called.

"Few more flakes," Owen answered.

Leeds threw two turns about the loggerhead and at once we began to settle by the bow. Cussing like a longshoreman, the Mate drew the hatchet from its beckets and tested the line with his hands.

"He's half a mile straight down," he muttered. "Stand by!"

He was about to bring down the hatchet when the line slacked.

"Haul away," he shouted. "Lively! He'll breach like a salmon!"

We hauled in, Owen flaking down as fast as he could. But there was no time to stow it in the tubs. All we could do was get it out of the way. And Lord help us if he ran again after he breached. We fisted it down between the afterthwart and the stern box in a tangle that would kill someone sure as shooting if we didn't watch it. It didn't seem much in the tub, but the riffle nearly filled the boat.

"Breaches!" the Mate yelled.

He came out of the sea like a leaping bass, clear of the water, and fell back like a church toppling over. His wave hit us like a deluge, and we fought for balance while he lay, our line still fast, blowing steadily, the spout drifting to us in evil-smelling vapor.

"Lay me on," the Mate said softly. "Sweetly now. Lay me close."

Leeds steered us clear of the slick and right over the flukes. We pulled to larboard of him, close so his mean little eye couldn't see us, until his sheer rose alongside like a sea wall.

"Bow me in."

Leeds swung on the steering sweep and we turned head on to him. The Mate drew the lance from its beckets under

the gunwale, slipped the guard from the murderous little blade, and shook free the short warp that secured the lance to the boat.

"Lay me for'ard of his hump!" he whispered.

We slid along the scarred mass, the bow actually scraping the black skin off the creamy blubber underneath. A sea broke against the whale and fell back into the boat. I sat and stared. I wasn't scared, I remember, then. I guess I didn't rightly appreciate the danger we were all in. It was as though I was in a front seat watching someone else in this crazy business of trying to kill a hundred-foot monster with a bodkin the size of a kitchen poker.

The Mate braced himself, sighted along the lance shaft, and lunged. Six feet deep it went, and the Mate swung like a mad monkey on the end of the pole, jerking it in circles to gash the insides of the whale and reach his "life." That's what we called the vital spot, which isn't, as you might think, the heart, but his lungs.

He didn't make it. The whale jumped like he'd been stung. His flukes rose and slammed down until we were bobbing in an acre of froth, gasping, half drowned, and blind as bats in the spray. Everyone was yelling at once. I was aware of that tangle of line about my feet. The whale rolled right under us, and his long thin underjaw with dozens of pointed peg teeth gnashed not a foot from our stern.

"Back and let him run!" the Mate ordered.

We jammed our paddles deep, and I saw the lance draw. The Mate hauled it in, jammed it straight in the bow cleat, and we jerked around as the line began to jump out of the tangle between me and Jimmy Owen.

" 'Ware line!" Jimmy shouted.

I crouched back against the gunwale as masses of tangled hemp rushed the length of the boat and shot overboard. By a miracle no one was taken, and soon as the line was clear, all hands began hauling in the bight for Owen to flake down. Then Leeds took a turn about the loggerhead and we slammed through the seas with the Mate in the bow, stiff as a figurehead.

The line tautened and smoked. I slopped water on it and felt the boat trembling with the strain on her.

Then we were in the middle of a pod of sperm, all blowing and breaching like a school of porpoises. Our whale slowed, and we pulled close. This time the Mate drove deep and reached his life. A hot gush of dark blood drenched us. We gave him line and he went into his flurry, smashing the sea, slamming his flukes until he rolled, fin out.

But he gallied the others. We were in the middle of tossing

flukes like one fly under half a dozen swatters. But we pulled close, the Mate cut loose from our irons and stabbed a waif into the dead whale to mark him as ours.

Then right alongside us came another sperm, scarred with circular squid wounds on his great tan-colored hump. He swung around us to nuzzle the dead whale. The Mate, without waiting to change ends, bent another iron on the line and let him have it. He sounded after sending us skidding like a kitchen plate with a blow of his flukes. He ran like a train, and I was half drowned with spray and wondering how we'd ever get back to the ship when he breached ahead.

"Lay me close," the Mate called. "Greasy luck, fellows. Lay me on, you sons!"

We hauled in, stowing the line every which way, past the ragged flukes, past the hump, and the Mate slid his lance in just abaft the eyefin, smooth as butter.

Next thing I knew I was turning end over end, high in the air. I hit water with a slap that knocked the wind out of me, soused under, and came up gasping. The flukes were over my head. I dived deep and swam until my lungs were busting. Then I had to come up.

The boat bobbed, keel up, the Mate clinging to it and cussing a blue streak. The whale was pitchpoling, his ram-like head bobbing out of the water so that his mean little pig eyes could find us. I paddled, still gasping, to the boat and hung on. I saw Jimmy Owen floating and dragged him close. Leeds stroked alongside, a cut along his head. Brava, dazed and wild-eyed, splashed to us. But we couldn't see Big Olaf. He couldn't swim, I remembered.

I lay low as I could, shivering like a sick pup, and trying to remember my prayers. Then there was a shout, and the Third Mate's boat ran down to us.

"Sheer off," the Mate spluttered. "Take the line; there the tub floats, and lance him before he runs. Ship'll pick us up!"

I sure hated to see the Third Mate take our line. He made fast and was running before we knew it.

Our boat was mashed flat amidships. That whale had bitten down on it like a deck hand on a hot dog. We wrestled her over and lashed the oars thwartships to make a raft, onto which we crawled. Our weight drove it under, and we crouched chest deep in water that felt suddenly cold.

"Anyone seen Big Olaf?" the Mate asked.

There was no answer. I began to feel really scared. It was growing dark and the sea was making. Owen and Leeds were feeling about the smashed timbers for a waif or something to signal with.

"Nothing here," Owen said. "Everything carried away when he stove us."

Seas began breaking over us as night fell. We had to hold fast to our lashings to keep the boat from going to pieces. Being the smallest, Leeds stood up and searched the darkness for lights.

"Nothing."

"Hold on," Mr. Nanton said. "Paddle to larboard. I smell that dead whale."

We worked with our hands until the sea suddenly smoothed and the air was full of an oily fishy reek. We bumped gently into something solid.

"Feel along 'til you find one of the irons. Then hold fast to it. This whale will make a lee for us."

Leeds found the end of an iron, and we took turns holding to it; there was no line to make fast with. Every now and then a sea broke right over the whale, but we were safe from the wind. We lay there an hour or so watching for a light. Then Pete Brava let out a scream and started splashing.

"Hold fast," Leeds gasped. "You tryin' to capsize us again?"

"Sharks!" Brava yelped. "Eatin' the whale. They're all around us."

Something hit the smashed boat and we soused under.

"Sheer off," the Mate ordered. "Splash around. Sing out."

We paddled hard as we could, the sinking boat sluggish, seas breaking over us, and lay to in the tossing blackness.

"All secure?" the Mate called. "You all right, Lester?"

"Aye, aye, sir," I said through my chattering teeth, cringing at the thought that a shark might touch me.

We waited, soaked and shivering.

"Listen!" Leeds said. "Heard something."

We strained our ears.

"Sing out. I think I heard a hail."

We hollered until we were hoarse as crows.

"Wait a bit and try again," the Mate said.

The black water rose and tossed about us until I began to think of those sharks and the awful depths of pitiless, drowning water with only a few shattered planks between me and death. Then I got a clip on the ear.

"What you dreamin' about, son," Owen said. "Stay awake, smack your arms about, and keep yerself warm."

I didn't like him hitting me. But I knew he did it to make me mad and stop me from being scared. One thing, my ear was warm. Then I distinctly heard a faint call.

"Dead ahead," Leeds said. "Make for it!"

We paddled again, crawling up the heavy seas and lurching into black depths, shouting as we got our heads above water. Again we heard a shout, nearer.

"Ain't no lights," Brava said. "It's gotta be Olaf!"

We moved on, and the shouts were closer. Then we heard him.

"Wait," Brava said. "We get big fellow like Olaf aboard, we swamp."

"We swamp then," Leeds said. "Give way."

"Help!" came from the darkness.

Then we heard splashing, and a sea carried him to us. He was sprawled out on his back on what was left of the boat floorboards.

"Easy now," the Mate said. "Softly, and we'll get you aboard."

He crawled, shivering and muttering, between me and Owen.

"Man, I thought I vos a goner," he said. "Vere's the s'ip?"

"That's what I'd like to know," the Mate growled. "If this wind don't go down, we'll never find out."

"You think they're looking for us?"

"Sure. We're close to that whale, and the skipper will be looking for the young 'un."

"That's something"—Owen chuckled—"though I'd trade him for a pannikin of Medford rum right now."

"How far to land?" Olaf asked.

"Bermuda's closest. About two hundred miles," the Mate told him.

"Lights," Brava shouted. "Hard abeam. Lights."

A reddish glint appeared and disappeared.

"The bark. Make for her."

We managed to turn and started paddling. The light came and went, scaring us half to death each time it vanished. Then suddenly it was clearer, and we yelled, spluttering as the sea slapped our faces.

"Man, they're cutting in," Owen said, sniffing.

We were close enough now to see cressets blazing, big iron baskets full of blubber chips, giving off a red flare that stained smoke from the tryworks.

"Why, those dirty——" Leeds said. "They didn't even look for us. Ahoy. *Canton*," he shouted. *"Canton!"*

Someone hailed us, and we saw a boat lowered. The Third Mate's boat ran down to us, and we carefully crawled aboard.

"We thought you was gone," the Third said. "Man, we searched everywhere!"

"Yeah. Well you didn't look far," Mr. Nanton snapped. "Didn't even find my whale."

"They said you was most likely dragged under."

"Well, we wasn't. Get's aboard before we perish."

"Who's that?" Captain Shockley was calling from the deck.

"Mate's boat," the Third called. "Stove."

We came alongside and crawled aboard. Captain Shockley was carrying on something awful about losing the gear and getting the boat stove. Anybody would have thought the Mate had stove us purposely. But he calmed down a bit when he heard of our whale.

"You better put over a boat and go bring him in," he said.

"My boat crew gets food and drink and a chance to rest," Mr. Nanton said, bold as brass. "Send someone else for the whale. Go for'ard, men!"

We stumbled over the slimy deck to the fo'c'sle while Mr. Nanton and Captain Shockley had words. But I was too thankful to care.

The deck was jammed with great steaming sheets of blubber slipping and sliding every which way. A great hook hauled a sheet of it inboard while men slashed it free of the carcass floating overside with knife-edged spades. Others were hacking it into long foot-wide strips and sliding it below into the blubber room. I got past somehow to where the tryworks were bubbling under the light of a cresset. The cooper ladled oil into cooling casks, and the Captain's boat steerer was forking slashed hunks of blubber into the trypots. Past them I ducked below, dragging off my wet clothes. Owen was behind me. He dipped into his sea chest for a black bottle. A swallow of that set me strangling and gasping, but it warmed me all the way down. Then Owen started rubbing the hide off me with a sheet of coarse toweling.

"Tumble in, sonny," he said, hoisting me into my bunk. "And thank your lucky stars for a mate with a heart. You're a real whaleman now you've been stove."

The *Canton* stank of the cooking blubber, feet thudded about the deck overhead, and the ship canted as the mighty blanket pieces were winched aboard. The greenies of the watch below crowded around with wide eyes, all talking at once, asking how we were stove. Pete Brava and Olaf were already snoring in their bunks.

"I didn't know whales were that mean," one of the kids said, looking uncomfortable.

"What would you do, s'pose someone sneaked alongside and stuck a pin in you?" Owen grinned. "Wouldn't you get mad? We were lucky. I've seen right whales smash a boat to flinders, then search around for the crew and smack down on them, deliberate as a cook tendering a slab of whale meat with a cleaver."

"What kind of fish is a right whale?" Nelson wanted to know.

"Ignorance!" Owen snorted. "Don't you greenies know nothin'? Whales ain't fish. They're warm-blooded, they breathe air through lungs, not gills, and they have young alive like other animals. They give milk, too. Also, whales is meat. They're animals. Savvy?" He got out his pipe, shaved off a fill of plug, and got it fired. "There's many different kinds of whales, too. But all us whalemen needs to know is about sperm, finback, right whales, humpbacks, and sulphur bottoms. Course, there's porpoises, blackfish—they're killer whales, nasty brutes—and belugas—they're little white whales the Eskimos hunt with their kayaks. The sulphur bottoms are the biggest. They're mean, and they got a bad habit of sinking if you don't get them alongside soon after they're killed. They grow down in the Antarctic waters, south of Australia and such. Right and bowheads are cold-water whales, too—up in the north Pacific and Arctic, finbacks, too. Humpbacks go to shallow water to have their young 'uns; they're easy to kill, but they don't have much oil or bone. Then there's a little Biscay whale. They used to catch them

WHALES

1. *Sperm*

2. *Humpback*

3. *Sulphur bottom*

4. *Finback*

5. *Right whale*

6. *Bow head*

off shore along Cape Cod and New England, drag them up on the beaches to try out their oil. Most valuable is the sperm: he's found all over in warm water, he's got the most bone and oil. But he's bad on account of his jaws. Remember this. Beware a sperm whale's jaw and a right whale's flukes."

"How come a right whale's flukes are so dangerous?"

"He can't see ahead and he ain't got no teeth, so he's got to fight with what he's got. He can cut flukes from one eye to the other. So you come on a right whale from ahead and a sperm whale from astern."

"How's a right whale feed if he ain't got no teeth?"

"Ain't you never heard of whalebone? It's a sort of strainer, hanging in a great fringe from his upper jaw. He feeds by opening his great mouth and swimming along through a sea of brit—that's a sort of tiny shrimp. He just keeps swimming until his big mouth is full of brit, little fish and weed and stuff, then he shuts it, squeezes the water out through the whalebone fringe, and keeps the food inside."

"What does a sperm whale eat?"

"He's different." You could tell Owen had a soft spot for sperm. "You wait until they get that sperm's jaw on deck. You'll see. He has teeth in his lower jaw only; sixteen foot long it is, and narrow as a scissors blade. It carries upward of forty pointed peg teeth of hardest ivory, that fit into holes in the upper jaw. Take a look at our boat and you'll see what he can do with those teeth. Sperm can't eat piddling little shrimps, nor can they go sweeping along the top of the water like scoop nets. They dive deep, do sperm, hundreds of fathoms deep, after the giant squids, tear them from their holding, and chop them up in bits small enough to swallow; a sperm whale has a mighty narrow throat. Makes you wonder!" he said thoughtfully. "A

sperm whale couldn't have managed to swallow Jonah on
account of his little throat, and a right whale couldn't have,
because of the whalebone strainer. I guess it was a sort of
sailor's yarn—about Jonah, I mean. Where was I?"

"About sperm whales eating giant squids."

"Oh, yes. Them squids are monsters over fifty foot long,
like great octopuses, only they got ten arms instead of eight,
all fitted with powerful suckers. They're strong, too. Sometimes they wrap them arms around the sperm and hold him
down until he drowns. I've seen sperm floating dead on the
surface and no mark on them except the round scars they got
from squid suckers. I'll bet if you look on the case of that
sperm they're trying out topside, you'll see squid marks; big
round circles like a hot plate might leave on the kitchen
table. A sperm whale is a fighter. He's got to fight to live.
Some folk say it's because a sperm whale's so fond of squid
meat that he gives ambergris. Worth more than its weight in
gold, that is, depending on quality."

"What is it?"

"It's used for making perfume; holds the scent in longer
than anything else. Some use it for incense, and them
Indian princes and rajahs use it for medicine. Queer thing
about the sweetest smelling thing in the world. It comes
out of a sick sperm whale, and only out of sperm. You
catch a sperm with thin wrinkled hide and poor blubber,
a weak spout and a powerful stink. Nine times out of ten
you'll find ambergris in him. It's in his innards and often
it's got squid beaks in it. People say the squid beaks hurt his
plumbing and the ambergris is a kind of growth to make it
hurt less."

"What's it like?"

"Sort of black and white, mottled. Feels waxy. When it's
cleaned, it has a sort of earthy, flowery smell. It's light,

floats, and sometimes people find it on the beach. Lots of it is found over in Bermuda, where the tides wash it in."

"Makes the sperm mighty valuable," someone said.

" 'Tain't the ambergris," Owen said. "You could spend a lifetime without seeing any. But the sperm oil is better than all other kinds, and inside a big hole in the sperm's head is spermaceti. You bail that out and it hardens like white wax, pure and clean as snow, it is. That's what makes the best candles; chemists make salves and ointments from it, too. Some foreign people make a butter substitute from it. Never goes bad."

"I'll take butter," Nelson put in.

"You'll take what you can get," Owen said sharply. "You'll be lucky if you see butter for the next couple of years. Porpoise oil on your hardtack will taste mighty good to you before you're much older."

"We gonna chase porpoises?"

"Sure. We're almost out of fresh meat now. Last pig was killed two days ago. We'll eat porpoise meat inside a week and be glad to get it. Porpoise, belugas, even sea elephant; they all give oil. And them terrible blackfish give the best of all. Used for watches and delicate instruments, blackfish oil is. Man, they used to put to sea off Provincetown on Cape Cod and chase blackfish ashore, then try 'em out on the beaches for their oil. Couple of barrels apiece some of them gave."

Owen was still talking when I fell asleep.

IV.

CUTTING IN AND TRYING OUT

Fire at sea . . . The Cassander *castaways . . . Abandoned in mid-ocean . . . Survival.*

I awakened at dawn in a fug of hot oil, sweat, smoke, tar, and fishiness. The *Canton* was listing steeply as the watch below staggered about in the half darkness, dragging on their few clothes. On deck the duty watch were like demons, black with smoke that billowed from the tryworks, their hair and beards matted with grease and their faces drawn with tiredness. The deck was ankle deep with gurry: slime, oil, and bits of black skin. Beside the fo'c'sle scuttle the jawbone of the whale they'd been trying out was lashed to the rail. It was as long as three men and narrow, armed with dozens of teeth that were white, pointed, and some of them over four inches long. It made me feel funny to think of those wicked things grinding down on our boat and mighty nearly biting me in two. Overhead the blubber hooks were swinging, and the 'tween deck was full almost to the main hatch with great sheets of steaming blubber that was stained with blood and bits of meat. The tryworks sent billows of smoke over the sails and across the dark sea; the cooper was ladling boiling oil into a cooling tank, and a boat steerer forked great lumps of blubber into the pots while one of the boys shoveled piles of tried-out scrap into the fires below. The cutting-in stage had been hauled up so that it stood at the starboard waist like a square-topped archway. And overside the skinned body of the whale was floating downwind in a sea of blood, with dozens of sharks charging in and wrenching great chunks of meat from it.

"Coffee—oh!"

I slipped and slithered aft with my pannikin and found Sam Thomas, the cook, hammering away at a slab of meat that was longer than his table.

"Whale steaks today, sonny," he said, slapping the toughness out of it with a mallet. "Good as any cow beef you ever cast a lip over. Here's your coffee. Now get outta me way!"

I gulped the hot molasses-sweetened coffee and picked my way to where our boat lay on the midships gallows. She was mashed flat, her planks splintered, the keel broken, and both gunwales stove in. Old Mr. Folger, the carpenter, was looking her over.

"Take four days to get her shipshape," he grumbled. "You fellers ought to be more careful. Cost a thousand dollars apiece, these do." He jutted his whiskers at me and glared through his spectacles like he thought it was my fault. I got for'ard quick.

By the tryworks Owen was yarning with the Mate, watching the bubbling, smoking pots. He saw me and tossed over a hot crisp curl of cooked blubber.

"Ever eat pork cracklin's, sonny? Here's a boat steerer's breakfast; whale cracklin's!"

It was good, not a bit oily or fishy. Then he lifted a dipper and took out of it a piece of hardtack that he'd been deep-frying in the blubber. It was crisp outside and soft inside.

"Only way to fix pantiles." He grinned. "Get that under your belt and you'll feel like a man."

I was swallowing the last of it and wondering if he had another when there was a yell from masthead, "Blo-o-o-ws. Blo-o-o-ws. Waif—oh!"

"That's our whale," Mr. Nanton shouted. "Where away?"

"Two points off the stern," lookout called. "Maybe a mile off, comin' out of the mist!"

"Hoist and swing."

We wrestled one of the spare boats overside, heaved short lines, boat spades, hooks, and oars into her, and slid down the falls to our places. The sea was calm, and we made good time over the waves until we pulled alongside the whale, floating like a derelict island.

"Them sharks did us out of twenty barrels." Leeds spat into the water. "Good thing we had another alongside to draw them off. They'd have foundered him else."

We rocked in his lee. Mr. Nanton lifted a boat spade, its four-inch blade sharp as a knife. Over the great flukes we rocked while he stabbed downward until a mass of black bone and gristle half as long as the boat floated free. Swiftly he cut away the other fluke.

"Get aboard, Pete," he ordered, "and make fast to his small."

Pete Brava slipped a line about his waist, took the spade, and jammed it into the narrow end of the whale as a holdfast. Then he stepped on to the slippery hide, clinging to the spade. Leeds passed him a weighted line, which he held while we maneuvered the boat until the line was under the tail stump. Then Brava made a running noose, sitting astride the small with the waves rolling over him. We hauled tight, made fast to the loggerhead, and Pete clambered back aboard.

"Give way, lads."

That carcass, three times as long as our boat, anchored us like a rock. We tugged until my eyes were popping out and at last got way on him.

"Easy all," Nanton said. "Ship's runnin' down to us."

We rested on our oars, and glad to.

"How come a whale swims head first and we have to tow him tail first?" I asked.

"Jaw hangs down when he's dead and slows him," Mr. Nanton said. "He tows easier stern first."

"Captain still mad at us?" Owen asked.

"No." The Mate grinned. "He was worried about his nephew. Second Mate was out looking for us all night. Missed us in the dark and thought we was lost. Captain pretended to be mad so he wouldn't show how gallied he was."

The *Canton* hove to close abeam of us, and the Second Mate's boat lowered to give us a hand in getting the whale alongside. A chain was hitched to the line about his small, hauled around, made fast, and drawn snug to the starboard side of the bark, with the head toward the stern. The cutting-in stage was lowered so that it stood about ten feet out from the ship's side above the whale. The ship maneuvered so that the whale was on the weather side. That way the wind pressure on the sails would balance the tremendous weight as the blubber was winched aboard and keep the vessel on an even keel.

Once secure, the whale tight against the ship's side, the hard work of whaling began. Mr. Reynolds, Second Mate, was lowered on to the whale by a monkey rope. With a half-round blubber spade he made a hole between the eye of the whale and the fin, about a third of the way down his body. A massive soft iron blubber hook, weighing a hundred pounds, was lowered and jammed into the hole. Meanwhile Captain Shockley and the Mate were out on the stage, slashing with wide spades until they'd cut through the blubber from the top of his head to the eye and around the fin.

HOW TO PEEL A WHALE

A. *Case*   B. *Junk*   C. *White Horse*   D. *Jaw*

Blubber hook is placed in hole chopped between eye and fin. Then, as cut is made from top of head and around fin, the hook is hoisted away. Weight of whale tears blubber free as you would strip a bandage from a finger.

"Haul away," the Captain called as Mr. Reynolds scrambled back to the deck. The triple blocks on the mainmast creaked as the biggest men aboard tugged the windlass bars. The chain tautened, and slowly the immense carcass began to lift. Swiftly the Mate slashed at the blubber until there was a dreadful tearing sound and the whale smashed back into the sea, his weight ripping the fin free. A strip of blubber eight inches thick and several feet wide was torn away from the carcass as the Mate chopped underneath to clear it from the meat, and the end of the scarf, as the strip is called, was lifted slowly to the blocks.

"Way 'nough," the Second Mate yelled.

The winchmen waited.

The Second Mate stood amidships behind the scarf. With

a boarding knife, a three-foot double-edged weapon, he stabbed two holes in the mass of blubber just above deck level. A second blubber hook was made fast. Then with the keen-edged knife he slashed through the blubber just above the hook and jumped for his life as the ponderous mass called a blanket piece swung inboard. Back to the main hatch it slid, carrying all before it until it was lowered into the blubber room 'tween decks.

"Heave away!"

The winchmen strained and the wide strip of blubber, now held by the second hook, continued to rise from the slowly turning whale.

"Hey, you!" the Captain shouted suddenly. "Git below to the blubber room and earn your keep."

I jumped lively, skidded around the scarf, and fell down the companion. In the 'tween decks there were sheets of blubber everywhere. Men slipped on it, clung to each other for balance, and threw themselves desperately out of the way of the descending blanket pieces. Two of them were carving the great sheets into blocks about two feet long and a foot wide.

"Hurry along them horse pieces," a hand shouted in the sweating, smoky, oily gloom lit only by stinking whale oil lanterns. A greenie heaved a horse piece onto a plank over a cask and another with a long blade with handles at both ends hacked it into one-foot blocks and cut each block down to the black skin in thick slices. Held together by the skin, these sliced blocks were called book pieces. On some ships, I learned later, the mates called for bible pieces, which meant the blubber was sliced thinner, for easier cooking. I was put to heaving the tubs of book pieces to a spot below the tryworks where they were hoisted up and forked into the pots. As each piece had all the oil tried out of it, it went into

Two whales alongside

Separating the head

Unrolling the "blanket"

Head of bull whale

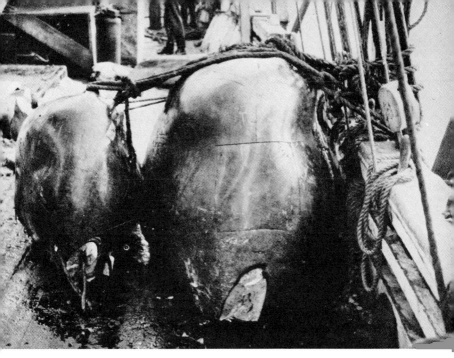

Two heads on deck

"Boarding blanket piece"

Lowering "blanket piece"

Last "blanket piece"

the fires under the pots—the best and cheapest of all fuels. Topside, the cooper was bailing the boiling oil into cooling tanks lashed along the rail.

All morning we toiled in that slippery nightmare. It was so hot and the blubber stank so, I was half sick. At noon I crawled on deck. They were still peeling that whale, the Captain cutting in a spiral the whole length of him, so that the scarf was unwound in a long unbroken ribbon like orange peel.

The sea was breaking over the whale, and huge sharks were under the stage, rolling on their sides to snatch great semicircular hunks out of the carcass. Every now and then the Mate dropped his spade on one and the gashed body writhed back in the sea to be torn to pieces by the others.

I went below before the Captain saw me. We were far ahead of the tryworks, which could only cook out about four barrels, that's 126 gallons of oil, an hour. Already there were several hundred gallons in the cooling tanks, and we had to stow the blubber anywhere we could reach.

My watch went below at six bells and I crawled back on deck. They'd almost finished stripping the carcass, were cutting off the small to use for eating and to render out the last drop of oil from the fluke stumps. But the head, most important part of a sperm, had to be taken aboard. I wondered how they'd do it. A sperm whale's head takes up a third of the whole body and accounts for almost half its total weight. That meant we had to get a mass weighing twenty tons aboard.

I watched the Mate cut two holes through the blubber close to the blowhole. A chain was passed through them and the hoist away signal given. As the massive head rose, men with spades hacked into the soft matter above the jaw until the case was torn free. Slowly it rose as the mast took the

The fighting jaw of the sperm whale being hauled aboard

tremendous weight, and the vessel listed until the stage was under water. Slowly the case came over the rail, was steadied, and lowered to the deck. Another chain made fast to the jaw, wrenched that off, and finally the toothed lower jaw was cut away and stowed on the foredeck.

Now the whale was cast off and the cutting-in stage secured.

The vessel listed so with the case aboard that the boilers were spilling over. Captain gave orders to clean them out. Case oil and spermaceti are more valuable than body oil and have to be cooked and stored separately.

I went to the case standing on end, lashed to the starboard rail.

"Off wit' yer duds," the Mate called. "Get inside that there case and bail."

Two of us, Nelson and I, had to strip down and get inside that hot greasy cavity. We bailed with a wooden bucket, clear whitish oil that smelled almost sweet. When we got that out, we had to scrape out the head matter with our hands. We were inches thick with grease. But we had to go on. We dropped the white spongy stuff into tubs which were carried to the tryworks and cooked out carefully. The junk, that's the rest of the head, was chopped into lumps to cook out the rest of the oil. Then the upper jaw was cut up to cook. It was dead white because there is no blood in the meat. So whalemen call it "white horse."

By the time we'd finished, half sick and tired to death, I heard the Mate say we had thirty-three barrels of pure spermaceti and case oil from the two sperm.

But I was ready to lie down somewhere and just die. The decks were almost knee deep with slime and oil, for the scuppers were plugged to save the precious stuff from flowing overboard. The greenies crawled to scoop up the gurry and store it in save-all casks. The tryworks still smoked as blubber came up from 'tween decks, but the upper deck was fairly clear now that the gurry was gone.

"All hands aft for rum," the Captain called.

They tumbled up, black as demons, from the blubber room. Nelson and I, scraping the grease off us with our hands, pulled on trousers and followed them to the afterhouse, where Captain Shockley had a big jug of rum and a tin cup. Each man took his tot and went back to work. When my turn came, my uncle looked at me a bit old-fashioned. But I took my tot and passed it to Jimmy Owen, who downed it and passed the cup back quick as a wink for his own. The Captain grinned and gave it to him.

We toiled in the blubber room until six bells in the second watch; then I crawled, filthy as I was, into my bunk. The fo'c'sle was a tangle of greasy clothing, brogans, pumps, and gurry that had leaked down through the deck. Olaf, who had finished six hours at the winch, groaned, dropped into his bunk, and started snoring at once.

For four days the tryworks smoked. The sails were black and oil seemed to sweat out of the deck planks. Below the stored blubber was beginning to rot, and the stench was enough to poison anyone but a whaleman. Some of the greenies were seasick all over again. I still don't know why I managed to hold my grub.

The cooling tanks were emptied fast as possible; casks were filled, headed up, and set chine to chine and bung up in the lower hold. Day after day the hands slipped and struggled with the great casks, and lookouts rode the hoops while we slaving greenies didn't know whether to hope they'd raise spouts or not. We had to get below and strip scraps of meat from the blubber and stow it in fat-and-lean casks. Later some unfortunate would have to pick the rotted meat out of the oil with his hands; for nothing with oil in it was wasted. It was five days from our striking whales before the oil was stowed below and the decks swabbed down with lippers, oblong pieces of blubber with hand holds cut in them; they acted as squeegees to swab up the last drops of precious oil from the decks. This dirty mess was ladled into a cask and left until the dirt settled and the clean oil could be put away.

In the bow the two jaws rotted, waiting until the teeth could be knocked out and shared among afterguard and foremast hands. The flat pan bones at the back ends of the jaws were sawed off and planed by Mr. Folger to be bleached and hardened for working. He told me that only the teeth and pan bones of the sperm whale can be used for scrimshaw. All other bones from sperm or right whales are too spongy with oil to keep.

I had no time to think of scrimshaw yet. I was set to helping Mr. Folger rebuild our stove boat; steaming cedar planks, clamping gunwales and strakes until she was good as new again. I was allowed to take my trick at the wheel, slush down the masts, tar cordage, and head irons with the boat steerers. It was warm enough to sleep on deck, well to windward of those rotting jaws, for the fo'c'sle was alive with cockroaches big as mice that ran all over us. Owen said they were drawn from their hidey holes by the rotted blubber and oil that soaked our soft timbers.

"They'll be shipmates until the end of the cruise, young-'un," he said. "Them and the rats."

I didn't mind, felt fine. We ate whale meat twice a day, great slabs of it. Like beef it was, in looks and taste except that it was a bit sweet. Cookie soaked it in vinegar to get rid of the oily taste.

"Hundred and twenty-four barrels," Mr. Nanton told us

when all was secure. "Maybe you brought us greasy luck, sonny."

I felt mighty proud. With my hundred and twentieth lay I had already earned one of those barrels of oil.

We turned out one morning to the loveliest sight I ever saw. The sea, smooth and limpid, had every wave edged with gold. The sky, full of broken clouds, was every color you could think of: purple, blue, red, yellow and, low down on the horizon, even green. The Mate was calling lookouts to the mastheads. I was about to start aft for my coffee when I saw something that chills the blood of a whaleman. There was smoke misting up between the hatch battens of the hold.

"Fire!" I yelled. "Fire!"

As I shouted, hands boiled up from the fo'c'sle in a smother of stinking vapor. The Mate came a'running. Captain Shockley, in his nightshirt, started for'ard.

"Buckets," the Second Mate called. "Get that hatch off!"

"Belay that," Mr. Nanton shouted. "Draft will bust it into flame. Line up men and pass buckets through the fo'c'sle alley. Lively, now!"

We dropped overside tubs, pails, anything that would hold water, hauled them up full, passed them from hand to hand down the fo'c'sle ladder and through the alley into the blubber room. At once there was a tremendous hissing, and the smoke shot up yellow and thick. The Second Mate rigged a leather hose to the for'ard pump. Mr. Coffin, Third Mate, poked his head out of the fo'c'sle scuttle.

"You can take the hatch off," he gasped, coughing. "Pile of oakum smolderin' like a red-hot mattress. Don't know how deep it's gone, but we got the top out."

The hatch came off and the hose was dropped into a billow of strangling smoke. Four hands caught the pump brakes and sea water pulsed down in a thick stream. At once the smoke was mixed with steam, rolling out like a volcano. We could hear shouting below and the clatter of gear. Men, half suffocated, crawled on deck, and others ducked below to keep the chain of buckets going.

"Keep the pump going 'til the smoke stops," Captain Shockley ordered. "Then lay all hands aft. We'll find out how fire got down there!"

It was over an hour before the fire was out. Then the black stinking mass of charred oakum was brought on deck and heaved overside. By noon all was secure and the pumps were taking out the water that almost filled the lower forehold.

We mustered aft of the midships gallows. Mr. Coffin was holding a lantern that had burst with the hot oil in it.

"Someone been sojering in the blubber room," he said. "Went to sleep in that oakum, likely, and knocked the lamp over. Anyone missin' from night watch?"

"Where's that Nelson?" Mr. Reynolds shouted.

We found him crouched in an empty bunk in the fo'c'sle.

"I didn't do nothin'," he yelped when we pulled him out. "Lemme be, I'm sick. I got fever. Lemme be. I just went in there for a rest like."

They dragged him, sniveling, aft.

"I bin missing a lantern two days," Dad Smith barked suddenly.

"I didn't take it," Nelson yelled.

"Why weren't you on watch?"

"I was sick. I crawled in there to rest. I didn't have no lantern. I blew it out!"

"Listen, you," Captain Shockley said. "Fire aboard a whaleship can mean death to all hands. Carelessness with pipe or lamp is the same as murder. What you got to say?"

"I didn't mean nothin'," Nelson whined.

"Six with the cat," Captain Shockley ordered. "All hands to witness punishment."

Nelson burst into howls of fear.

Even the lookouts were called down. We mustered along the larboard rail, some of the hands whispering that six strokes wasn't enough for a longshore rat who played with his shipmates' lives. Nelson crouched by the tryworks, glaring about him like a wild thing. The Mate went below and came up with a length of line split up into several knotted strands.

"Take off your shirt," he ordered.

"No," he screamed, clutching himself. "I ain't done nothin'. It was that Mosher. I seen him. I seen him go in there."

Two boat steerers grabbed him, stripped him to the waist, and lashed his wrists to the cutting-in-stage rigging. He hung there kicking, screaming.

"You ain't been touched yet," the Mate said disgustedly. "Hold still and take your medicine."

I felt a bit queer to see a grown man flogged. He was struggling like a hooked fish, his face wet with tears, screeching and cursing something awful. The Mate stepped to one side of him, ran the cat through his fingers, and looked at the Captain.

"One!"

The lines smacked across the bare white back. Nelson flinched like he'd been shot and yelled, his mouth wide open. Red stripes rose across his shoulders.

"Two!"

Again the cat swished. He bawled, sounds I never thought a man could make.

"Three!"

He was striped from shoulders to waist, moaning and choking as he struggled.

"Four!"

The Mate barely touched him.

Nelson howled, spittle running down his chin, his eyes starting.

"Cut him down," Captain Shockley said in disgust.

Nelson fell on the deck, wriggling in agony, his whole body twitching as he squealed and cursed, threatening all of us with dreadful things.

"Stow your dirty gab," the Mate said. "You ain't hurt. Slop some water on him!"

Nelson howled again as the cool sea water hit. But the skin wasn't broken.

"Put some salve on him!"

The cook smoothed ointment on the wealed back, and Nelson tried to bite his hand. He was hiccuping with fright and pain, making high moaning sounds and spitting out filth.

"Now get for'ard," the Mate ordered.

Nelson got to his feet, snatched his shirt, and ran to the fo'c'sle. He'd stopped screaming now it was all over.

"Men," Captain Shockley said. "You've seen something I never thought to order. I'm not a hard case captain and I don't hold with flogging aboard my ship. But any man who thinks so little of his mates as to leave them to do his work and risk their lives in the bargain deserves strict punishment. That's all. Lay to, Mr. Nanton."

"Masthead," the Mate called. "Watch on deck, to your work!"

It was my trick at the hoops with George Leeds. We swung there, watching the calm and empty sea without talking.

"He ain't much good," Leeds said after a while, "but maybe that little taste of the cat will help him to be a whaleman. He's lucky at that. I've seen foremast hands with their ribs laid bare for less than what he done."

I still felt badly. I'd seen boys flogged at school; I'd been flogged myself, and marked worse than Nelson. But I'd never seen a grown man grizzle and carry on like that.

"We'm lucky at that," Leeds said soberly. "All soaked with oil, we could have gone up in no time, like the *Cassander* did."

The *Cassander,* he told me, sailed out of Providence, Rhode Island, under Captain Henry Winslow in November, 1847. She had a small crew, only twenty-four, and two of them were African Negroes she'd picked up in the Western Islands. She took some right whales and shipped home 1500 pounds of baleen.

By the first of May, 1848, she was headed west across the South Atlantic toward the Off River Grounds. The Negroes had been behaving a bit queer, but there was no time to think about them, for she struck heavy weather. A moderate gale was blowing one afternoon and all hands were taking in sail when smoke was seen coming out of the fo'c'sle hatch.

All hands were called down. But there was no chance. The fore part of the ship was ablaze.

"Man the pumps!" the Mate shouted. "Get water into the forehold; there's four barrels of tar down there!"

"Man overboard!" the steersman yelled. "Two of 'em!"

The two Negroes were trying to swim in the heavy seas. Captain Winslow heaved a line to them.

"Catch aholt!" he shouted. "We'll have you aboard in jig time."

But the men refused the line, swimming wildly away from the ship.

"Scared of the fire," Captain Winslow said. "Get a boat over, Mister."

"Hoist and swing!" the Mate shouted.

His boat dropped into the sea, and the men rowed short strokes in the broken water after the two bobbing heads. Then one disappeared in a pink foam.

"Get the other."

The Mate reached for him. The Negro fought him off, sobbing. Finally one of the crew stunned him with an oar and they pulled him aboard.

"Back to the ship before she burns to the keel," snapped the Mate. "Give way!"

The Negro crouched amidships, shivering and moaning while the boat pitched toward the blazing *Cassander*. They climbed aboard, but it was too late. The crew toiled hopelessly while yellow flames licked up the foresails and choking smoke drifted to them on the powerful wind.

"Can't make the pumps, sir," the Second Mate gasped.

"Get the boats over," Captain Winslow shouted. "Put food and water into them. We'll have to abandon."

Steerage, where stores were kept, could not be reached for the poisonous smoke. They got what bread and water was in the galley and lowered it into the boats along with clothing, a few tools, and navigating instruments. Then the whole crew, twenty-three now, climbed down into them, rowed clear, and watched their ship burn to the water's edge and disappear in a billow of black smoke.

They passed lines between the three boats and rode out a screaming storm that lasted all night. By daybreak, drenched and fearful, they heard the Captain plot their position as latitude 34 degrees, 40 minutes south, and longitude 45 degrees, 50 minutes west.

"That puts us four hundred miles from the nearest landfall," the Captain told them. "Check what stores we got."

There were fifteen pounds of hard biscuit, ten gallons of water, and a little salt horse from the harness cask. The captain did some figuring.

"With luck and the Lord's help we'll raise land in two weeks," he said soberly. "That'll give us a gill of water a day for each man; that and a piece of hardtack. We'll keep the meat for broth in case of sickness."

"Me, I'd like to know what started that fire," the Mate said. "Why'd it have to break out in the forehold; nobody had no rights down there. And it was too far gone before we could fight it. Captain Winslow, it's my belief that fire was started."

"Who done it?" The hands glared at each other; all but the Negro, who crouched, head down, in the Captain's boat.

"What ails him? Hey, boy, did you set that fire?"

"Yes, sah." The Negro faced his Captain. "My bruddah make fire!"

Those in his boat started over the thwarts for him. But the Captain faced them off.

"Starn all!" he snapped. "No sense in more killing. Maybe we'll all be dead before long. What made you do it, boy? We been good to you, ain't we?"

"Yessah, Cap'in. You good too much. But Bruddah hear you say we go 'Merica-side. He fear you go sell we for slaves. So he fire ship and we jump in sea. Think we drown while you fight fire. No mean kill fine ship. We want die, dassall. Bruddah cut heself with knife before he jump. That's why he sink so quick."

"Heave him overside," a hand growled. "He don't rate food and water after what he done."

"He'll take his chance with the rest of us," Captain Winslow declared. "Don't you fret none, boy. You won't never be no slave while I got any say. Now, all hands. Pass lines from boat to boat. Course is due west. I'll lead. Wind's against us. So out oars and give way!"

The three boats climbed over foam-laced waves and slid down into their troughs. On each crest they teetered, lashed by icy spray. In the troughs there was, for blessed seconds, respite from the wind. All day the men pulled, sick as dogs in the plunging boats, crowded, cursing, bailing, spelling each other as hands cracked with salt, slimed the oar looms with blood. And always the wind, vicious and pitiless, forcing them back into the empty wastes of the South Atlantic.

By night all were exhausted, so the Captain ordered sail, and boat headers tried to hold as close to the wind as possible, risking capsizing at every tack.

For four days they struggled, drawing each evening to the Captain's boat for their pitiful mouthful of water and piece of hardtack. They couldn't tell their direction, for the sky was too overcast for Winslow to take sights. But the wind held steady and he figured it had not changed.

On the morning of May 5 a hand in the Captain's boat struggled to his feet, balancing wildly in the bow.

"Sail!" he gasped through salt-cracked lips. "Sail ho! Blo-o-ws! Blo-o-o-ws!"

"Haul him down," someone groaned. "He's crazed!"

"No!" the man sobbed. "Starboard beam. Sail ho!"

"I see him," the Mate yelled as his boat rose to the crest of a sea. "Sail ho!"

Now they made out the top hamper of a vessel far to the north.

"Oars!" the Captain called. "Give way. Sweetly now. Put your backs into it. Spring, my bullies. We're saved!"

The boats cast off from each other, each one heading for the sail.

"Food, water, and hot rum, my hearties," the Mate shouted. "Stroke, stroke, stroke. Spring your backs out, my lucky lads!"

The Mate's boat drew ahead, a hand in the bow frantically waving his tattered shirt. Slowly the boats crawled over the sea until they were close enough to recognize a brig under reduced sail.

"Back your yards!" the Captain bawled until he was hoarse. "Brig ahoy. Help!"

The vessel ignored their signals.

"Give way!" the Mate yelled. "They ain't seen us!"

The brig, tacking against the head wind, reached toward the boats. The Mate, far ahead, ran under her beam.

"Brig ahoy!" he shouted. "Heave us a line. Castaways!"

A man with gold earrings looked down at them and shouted, waving them off.

"A Spaniard," a hand yelled.

The Mate snatched at a trailing line and was towed astern of the vessel. He read the name *"Alercidita,* Barcelona," on her counter.

"Ahoy!" he shouted. "Blast your eyes, we'm shipwrecked. Where's your captain?"

Captain Winslow's boat made fast to the Mate's. Two men peered at them from the stern of the brig.

"What you wan'?"

"Where's your captain?"

A fat man in dirty oilskins shouted something.

"He Captain Dominick," the other shouted. "What you' name?"

"Captain Winslow, the ship *Cassander* out of Providence. Burned at sea. Americanos. Let us aboard!"

"No got room," the interpreter shouted, after exchanging words with Dominick.

"No room?" Winslow gasped. "We're shipwrecked mariners, Mister. Take us aboard!"

"No can do!"

"Where you bound?"

"Montevideo."

"Captain, my men are starving. Won't you take us to your nearest port?"

"No got room!"

Several seamen lined the rail, grinning down at the whalemen.

"Blasted heathen," the Mate growled. "Give us a tow, then."

"No. Bad weather come up. You cast off!"

Winslow had his men haul close, and with a wild leap, managed to board the brig.

"Go back!" The Spaniards crowded threateningly. "Get off. You got no right aboard we."

"Look, Captain. We'll pay you soon's we make land. Let us aboard for a little while, a night maybe, enough to give my men a rest. Give us food and water and we'll go back to our boats. We'll never make it if you don't help us."

"No. You go back!" The crew were moving in, some carrying handspikes.

"Will you give us food and water?" Winslow begged desperately. "For God's sake, don't abandon us."

"No got food, water. You go back!"

Winslow eyed the puffy features of Captain Dominick.

"Mister," he said quietly. "In all my years at sea I never thought to meet a master who'd abandon men to drown. We're twenty-three souls in open boats, at the mercy of wind and water. If we die, our blood is on your greasy head. But if we make port, Mister, I tell you, I won't forget you!"

"Go back!" The Captain waved dirty hands. "Go back!"

Captain Winslow managed to reach his tossing boat and they cast off, watching the brig, her crew jeering at them, draw rapidly away.

"Well, men," Winslow said. "We're abandoned. But we ain't finished. No, sir. Not by a long dart. Draw nigh and we'll offer up a prayer to God, since that imitation of a man won't help us!"

They prayed, some silently, some aloud, their wretched faces haggard with despair.

"Give way!"

They leaned on their oars, slowly climbing the billows and sinking into their depths. That night fierce squalls beat down on them until half the men in each boat crouched along the weather rails as breakwaters while their mates bailed for their lives. But the seas smashed over them, driving the boats astern faster than the oars pushed them forward.

"Heave to," the Captain shouted.

They lashed their oars in bundles and tossed them overboard on long lines to act as sea anchors. All night they lay pitching in the roaring blackness, each man holding on with one hand while he bailed with the other.

Dawn came, chill and gray. Wearily the men drew in the sea anchors. The squalls moderated and they set spritsails, tacking weakly against the gusty wind. Then a gale roared down from the northeast. They had to lie to their sea anchors again, soaked, in agony from sea boils, holding hands before their parched mouths to keep out the fatal sea water. The gale worsened until a mighty sea came brawling over the others and smashed square down on the Captain's boat. All hands held on, gasping, drowning, breathless under the weight of water. When the wave passed, their boat, swamped, sank under them.

"Help!"

They struggled feebly in the yeasty seas, weighted down by their clothing, too weak to fight long. But the remaining two boats surged down to them. It was night before the drowning men were divided between the boats headed by the Mate and Second Mate.

"Now we're done for," a hand muttered. "What water and food we had's gone with Captain's boat. No compass, neither. We're lost!"

But they crawled on, twelve men in the Second Mate's boat; eleven, including Captain Winslow, in the Mate's. The gunwales were six inches from the sea, taking in water at every oar stroke. They lashed the boats together to ride out the storm, praying for help.

The night was wild; black, glistening seas rising to smash down on them with phosphorescent foam. Several times they gave themselves up for lost. But before dawn the wind slackened, and then the sun came up and they knew their prayers had been answered. The sky was blue, filled with tiny clouds, but the sea, still rough from the storm, pounded them relentlessly. They cut adrift and bailed, sliding over waves that threatened to swamp them.

The sky clouded over.

"Lay to," the Captain called wearily. "This is the end."

But there was no wind, only rain, blessed rain, torrenting down on them until the waves were mashed flat. Laughing, spluttering, they lay back, mouths open, gulping in the sweet water. They spread sails and oilskins to catch the precious liquid, their strength coming back as the water soaked into their tissues.

By noon the sea was calm, the wind veered around to the

south. Painfully they set their sails, and the two boats moved heavily toward the east.

The weather held fair until May 10, when they sighted land. None hailed it. Some wept a little. And the Negro shouted thanks in an unknown tongue. Steadily they approached the coast. There was a cape, a belt of dark trees, and a line of surf. Helplessly the boats drifted toward shore.

"Stand by," Winslow called as the ground swell lifted them.

Boat headers stood at the stern oars to guide the heavy-laden craft through the breakers. The Captain's boat rose on a glistening comber and, her men rowing desperately, was carried on its crest until the keel touched sand and they tumbled out, to haul feebly at the boat that had saved them, to keep it from being dragged back by the undertow.

The Mate's boat was less lucky. The men, too weak to race the combers, were caught, breached, and rolled over and over, until they were cast up on the beach. The Captain's crew pulled them clear, and all hands dropped thankfully on dry land.

All but one. After they had rested, Captain Winslow called a muster. A man was missing. They staggered down to the water to where the body of the Captain's boat steerer, too weak to swim through the mountainous surf, lay, drowned.

"We who are left will give thanks," Captain Winslow said.

Heads bowed, they knelt in the sand.

There some Brazilians found them and carried them to the fishing village of Conventus, near Cape Santa Martha Grande. They were fed and given places to rest while runners were sent to the nearest American agent.

When they reached him, they laid their complaint against Captain Dominick of the brig *Alercidita* of Barcelona.

Questioned later, the Spaniard had the gall to say that he had offered the whalemen passage to Montevideo and that *they had refused!*

"You think that twenty-three men, without food and water, riding a gale in open boats, would refuse help?" Captain Winslow inquired quietly.

Whether Captain Dominick was ever punished for his cold-blooded callousness, no one ever heard.

But I sure wouldn't have liked to be in that Spaniard's *espadrillas* if Captain Winslow ever caught up with him.

V.

EXPLORING THE SEVEN SEAS

*Discovery of the Gulf Stream . . . Captain Whit-
field and Mungo John . . . Opening Japan's door.*

DURING MY FIRST cruise in the *Canton* I hardly ever
spoke to my uncle, Captain Shockley. It was only during
my tricks at the wheel that he addressed me with anything
more than an order. Tommy Brown, the cabin boy, would
secure a chair in the angle of the afterhouse and the taffrail,
the Captain would come on deck, glance at the compass, take
a turn about the quarter-deck, study the weather, then come
aft and settle himself. After his pipe was going well, if the
cook was too busy to listen in, he would talk to me. I paid
attention, for though he was a man of few words, what he
said was like good food; it stayed with me and was mighty
nourishing.

"Mate gives a good account of you," he said one proud
afternoon. "Seems like you might make a whaleman yet."

"I hope so, sir," was all I dared answer.

"It's a fine trade; used to be third biggest in the United
States. It's a trade you can be proud of, for it was the whaling

trade that made our grand country what she is. Our whaleships opened up the remotest islands, our anchors tasted the
mud of the ports of the world. We led the way into the wild
places of the Pacific and the missionaries followed with the
Word. When explorers went out looking for new seas, they
usually took a whaleman along to show them the course.
For when the *Blossom,* fitted out with the best gear and
manned by scientists, went looking for the North Pole back
in 1840-odd and was forced to turn back above the seventy-
first parallel, she found that the *Saratoga* of New Bedford
had gone fifteen miles nearer the Pole; and that, in the
ordinary course of chasing whales! Russian and British ex-
peditions, getting ready to plant their flags in the Antarctic,
found that New England whaleships had been there before
them. Our Navy charts were drawn from whalemen's logs,
and if it hadn't been for us, the United States would be a
different place. Why, but for the sea-learning of whalemen, New York City might not even be on the map today—
as an important port, that is."

It sounded a bit farfetched to me. But I knew my uncle
didn't talk without knowing what he was saying. So I kept
my eye on the compass card and waited.

"Back in the early days," he went on, "there was a con-
siderable feeling between the British and American seamen.
And one thing the British couldn't understand was why our
little merchant ships were beating the big English packets
across the Atlantic. The merchant vessels from England to
Rhode Island got there fourteen days, and more, sooner
than the packets that plied between England and New York.
The packet people couldn't make it out. They had meetings,
fired captains, altered their vessels. But it made no difference.
They lost business hand over fist, for passengers found it
quicker to go to Rhode Island by ship and on to New York

by coach instead of going direct to New York by packet. So they figured that the only possible thing to do was make Rhode Island the chief packet port instead of New York.

"The New York merchants and shipping agents began to kick and scream. They had mighty investments in New York; their trade would be ruined and the fine city on the Hudson would dwindle away to nothing. So they took their troubles to Benjamin Franklin, who was their agent in England.

"Old Ben was no fool. He did some careful thinking and asking around. He was pretty sure that some shrewd New Englanders were putting something over on the British, but he wasn't sure what. So he sent for a relative of his, Captain Folger of Nantucket, a whaleman who happened to be in London at the time.

" 'What do you know about this business, Captain Folger?' he asked.

"Captain Folger looked down his nose.

" 'Well, sir,' he said at last. 'Most of the merchantmen are commanded by New England whalemen. They know the ocean better than those packet-ship masters. Y'see, Benjamin, there's a current several miles wide flowing a few miles off the American coast. From way down in the Mexican Gulf, it runs about three miles an hour, almost parallel to the coast as far's Nantucket, then up to Newfoundland, and there turns east. Its drift reaches to Britain and up to Norway, even. Now, sailing west, a whaleman knows he's got to steer clear of that current or it'll hold him back; in light winds he'd maybe even go astern. So the Rhode Island ships avoid the current until they have to cross it close to port. The packet ships buck the current all the way west. That's how they lose time.'

" 'How come the British don't know about this current?'

" 'We've told 'em, Benjamin, we've told 'em. But them

packet captains is too high and mighty to take advice from us simple American whalemen.'

" 'Well, trade will be finished in New York if we don't do something about it. So just you sit down, Captain Folger, and draw me a chart of that current so I can show it to the British. Maybe they'll take some advice from me.'

"Captain Folger made a chart showing how to ride the current and how to steer clear of it. And this is what Benjamin Franklin wrote about it:

" 'The Nantucket whalemen, being extremely well acquainted with the Gulph Stream, its course, strength and extent, by their constant practise of whaling on the edges of it, from their island quite down to the Bahamas, this draft of the stream was obtained from one of them, Captain Folger, and caused to be engraved on the old chart in London for the benefit of Navigators by B. Franklin!' "

After the war, my uncle told me, it was a whaleship, the *Bedford* of Nantucket, that was first to show England the Stars and Stripes. Her cook, who was humpbacked, went ashore in London to see the sights. He hadn't gone far before a limey sailor slapped him on the hump and said, "What ho, mate. What you got there?"

"Bunker Hill and be dammed to ye," the cook yelled. "Will ye try to mount her?"

Truly speaking, it was a whale more than a whaleman that found out what explorers had been trying to learn for hundreds of years: whether or not there was a northwest passage between the Atlantic and Pacific oceans.

The *Cornelius Howland,* of New Bedford, took a large whale off Point Barrow in the Arctic Ocean, on the Pacific side. While they were cutting in, they came across, all healed over in the blubber, a harpoon with the initials A.G. stamped into the head. Now every ship puts her private mark on her irons, to save trouble in case two ships are after the same whale. And when the *Cornelius Howland* reached home port, she found out that that iron had been darted by the *Ansel Gibbs,* also of New Bedford. But it had been darted in the Davis Straits in the Atlantic Ocean! Now if that mighty whale had been able to find his way around the North American Continent (those polar whales never cross the Equator), there must be room for a ship to go around. But no one was certain until that time.

It was Captain Shockley who told me how a whaleman was one of the chief forces in opening Japan to the world.

Since 1641 Japan had been shut off from the rest of the world. The shoguns, war lords, governed the country. There was an emperor, but he was at Kyoto, a long way from the shogunate at Yedo, as Tokyo was called then, so the war lords controlled the whole land.

Portuguese and Dutch missionaries had come in and converted many Japanese to Christianity. And the traders, as usual, weren't far behind the missionaries. The shoguns, watching the spread of Christianity and seeing how the people clamored for trade, were afraid their power would be undermined by all the foreigners and their improvements. So they got their armies together and massacred every foreigner they could find. Churches were destroyed, books burned. They wanted nothing to do with the outside world. No Japanese were permitted to leave their boundaries. No ships large enough to leave the coastal waters were allowed to be built. If any Japanese fisherman, blown out to sea, tried to get back to land, he got his head chopped off.

But the shoguns didn't want to cut themselves off entirely from foreign trade; there were silks and drink and other things, too good for the common people, that they wanted for themselves. So they allowed some Chinese and a few Dutchmen to build go-downs on the little island of Deshima, which was a patch of man-made land in the harbor of Nagasaki, joined to the mainland by a bridge. They weren't allowed off the island without special permission and under guard. No Japanese could even talk to them except in the presence of one of the Shogun's men. The Japanese kept the keys of the go-downs. Those ships allowed into harbor were boarded and searched. Guns, powder, and rudders were removed and the sails locked. They were kept under strict guard until their cargoes were discharged and they were reloaded with copper, gold, and such. The Dutch and Chinese were prisoners on their little island. The Japanese insulted them; even beat them. But they took it; their profits more than made up for a few bruises.

As the years went by, other foreigners tried to reach the Japanese. A delegation of missionaries from Macao reached the mainland. The leaders and fifty of the followers were beheaded and the rest sent back with messages that the Japanese wanted nothing from the outside world. They would slaughter all foreigners, even their kings. And if He attempted to land in Japan, even God Himself!

Sometimes foreign seamen were wrecked on the Japanese coast. Most were killed at once. Some were allowed to live. They were paraded through the towns like animals, beaten, mobbed, and stoned. Sometimes they were kept in bamboo cages too small for them to stand, sit, or lie in. Finally they had to stamp and spit on the Cross before they were handed over to the Dutch in Deshima, more dead than alive.

So our ships, though they hunted whales in the Japan Grounds, gave that country a wide berth.

One of them was the bark *John Howland,* whose captain was William H. Whitfield of Fairhaven, just across the

Acushnet River from New Bedford. He was a stout, dark-bearded, quiet man, much respected by his crew.

In the spring of 1841 they were hunting whales not far from the Ryukyu Islands. But the crew were uneasy being so close to the bad shore, and Captain Whitfield gave orders to change course for the China Sea.

The lookout in the mainmast hoops hailed one morning.

"Land! Land ho!"

"Where away?"

"Larboard beam!"

Captain Whitfield got his glass on a tiny speck that was hardly visible in the fog and rain.

"We need recruitment," the cook mentioned. "Fresh meat wouldn't go so bad."

"Heave her to, Mister," Captain Whitfield ordered. "Send in two boats and see if you can pick up fresh meat, greens, and water."

Some hours later the boats returned. Captain Whitfield stared at five naked, shivering figures crouched between the thwarts of the Mate's boat.

"Nothing there, sir," he reported. "Found these castaways. They're starving."

"Fetch them aboard," Captain Whitfield ordered. "Give them blankets and bunks in the fo'c'sle. Cookie! Send food for'ard. Tell them we won't hurt them."

The five ate like wild animals, gulped hot coffee, and crouched away from the advances of the watch below.

"Far's I can make out," the Mate reported, "they'm Japanese fishermen. Blown out to sea months ago and wrecked on that island. No sign of their vessel, though. Broke up, I guess. What do we do with them, Captain?"

"We can't land them in their own country," Whitfield said, "and that's a fact. They'd get their heads chopped off for leaving Japan waters. We'll give them passage to Honolulu when we put in to send home our oil. The Mission will care for them."

That night Captain Whitfield wrote up his log:

"Sunday, June 27, 1841.

"This day light wind from S.E. Isle in sight at 1 P.M. Sent in two boats to see if there was any turtle, found five poor distressed people on the isle, took them off. Could not understand anything from them than that they was hungry. Made the latitude of the isle 30 deg. 31 min. N."

For three days four of the castaways lay in their bunks. But the fifth, a taut, stocky young fellow of around fourteen, was all over the ship, his bright eyes everywhere, chattering like a magpie while he studied all the things he'd never seen before.

As the vessel moved east, the young Jap made himself at home, trying to talk English, pointing to things and telling their names in his own tongue, until the crew made him a sort of pet. His name was Manjiro Nakahama. But all they could make of it was Mungo John.

He didn't care what he did so long as it was work. He helped the sailmaker, fetched and carried things for the carpenter, turned the grindstone while the boat steerers put edges on harpoon heads and boat spades, helped the cook, anything. And when the *Howland* stood in to Honolulu harbor, Mungo John begged to stay aboard.

"Me good boy," he said eagerly. "Work hard. No send me away-go. Work hard. Do all things."

"He's a bright one," the Mate said. "Cheerful, too, with that grin."

"All right." Captain Whitfield smiled. "You stop along me. Cabin boy. Savvy?"

"Savvy!" John dropped down on his hands and knees and tried to put the Captain's foot on his head.

"Hey! Belay that! I want a cabin boy, not a footstool."

Mungo John was a good investment. He kept the galley cleaner than it had ever been, mended the Captain's clothing, even did his washing. He repeated everything spoken and practiced his English on the crew until he had them in fits of laughter.

It was May 7, 1843, when the *John Howland* got back to New Bedford. By then Mungo John could talk English almost as well as any of the crew. He stared about him at wonders he'd never dreamed of: great tall houses, horses bigger than any he'd seen, great steam-puffing trains, and hundreds of ships. But what interested him most were the Americans. They weren't the foreign devils he'd heard tell of, they were big, warm, cheerful folk who welcomed people instead of chopping their heads off.

He went to live at Captain Whitfield's house in Fairhaven. He could hardly believe it. It was like a palace compared to the only home he'd ever known. And when the Captain went whaling again, Mungo John was sent to school in New Bedford.

One thing puzzled him. What was the magic that helped Americans to find their way, without sign or mark, across the wide and empty oceans? Captain Whitfield, next time home, gave him a copy of Bowditch's *Navigator,* and Mungo John studied that in every minute of his spare time. Not that he had much. He was working at the cooper trade between lessons and his study of navigation.

In 1846 he was about eighteen and felt himself a man. He read in the Boston *Enquirer* about Commodore Biddle's trip to Japan and his offer of American friendship and trade. He read how the Shogun had insulted the Americans in

Yedo Bay. Manjiro felt he had lost face. If only the Japanese people could know about America. He went to Captain Whitfield about it.

He wanted to go home, he said. He wanted to see his old mother, of course. But he wanted just as much to tell his people about how they were missing all the good things that America offered them.

"But you know," Captain Whitfield told him, "they'll kill you if you try to go back."

"Maybe so, maybe not so," Manjiro said. "But I must go back."

"Well, you're a stout chap and a fair cooper. I'll see what I can do."

Captain Whitfield arranged for him to ship as cooper in the bark *Franklin,* under Captain Davis. But the Captain took sick and the *Franklin* came home without going near Japan.

"Can't be sure of a whaleship," Captain Whitfield told Mungo John. "We follow the whales. Lookee, why don't you ship on a Pacific whaler?"

This was 1849, and almost every whaler that put in at San Francisco that year was deserted for the goldfields. Maybe Manjiro found himself in an empty ship, for he went to the goldfields and panned himself enough to buy passage to Honolulu and a bit over.

He had letters from Captain Whitfield saying what he planned to do. He showed them to the U.S. consul and to the Reverend Samuel C. Damon, of the Seaman's Bethel. First he had to find the men who'd been rescued with him, if he could. Well, one of them was dead, but he found the other three, and they promised to go back with him.

He bought himself a good whaleboat, fitted her with navigation instruments—compass, sextant, and the like—loaded books and presents for his mother aboard. Then, thanks to Captain Whitfield's letter, he was able to get passage for himself, his friends, and his boat on a merchantman bound for Shanghai. The Captain promised to put him, his friends, and the whaleboat overside as close to Japan as he dared go.

One evening, in a blinding snowstorm, the boat was lowered some four miles off the coast of one of the Ryukyu Islands. The four Japanese dropped anchor and crouched in the icy darkness to wait for morning. They had gone too far to retreat. Before them perhaps death waited. Being converted to Christianity, they prayed.

Next dawn they rowed in to a sand beach. There was no one in sight. They were unloading their gear when a yelling mob came racing down from behind the dunes. Guards knocked them down and irons were clamped about their wrists and ankles and they were left without food and water until authorities summoned from the nearest town came to bark questions and stare at the strange instruments they had brought. Manjiro, obviously the leader, was unable to satisfy them; he had almost forgotten his native tongue. He was taken away from his friends and thrown into jail to wait, judging by his captors' threats, torture and execution.

For six months he lay half starved, beaten, and without news. Then they kicked him aboard a small vessel and he was taken to Nagasaki. The local governor sent for him and demanded to know what the strange instruments were for. Manjiro tried to explain the compass and sextant. They refused to believe him, and he was thrown back into jail.

Meanwhile an American whaleship, the *Lagoda* of New Bedford, was wrecked on the Japanese coast. Eighteen men were captured and driven into the interior. One of them, brutalized by Japanese torture, committed suicide. Others died of hardship and their wounds.

The U.S.S. *Preble* anchored off Nagasaki and threatened to shell the place unless the prisoners were released. The Shogun promptly handed them over. But the governor sent for Manjiro in a terrible rage.

"You are a spy," he yelled, "sent by the foreign devils who come with guns to make war on us, to destroy us!"

"Not so," Manjiro answered bravely. "They are devils only if you hurt their people. In America all men are equal!"

"Lies. How can all men be equal?"

But Manjiro's defiance made them nervous; they were afraid to kill him outright. And for two and a half years they kept him in jail, trying with all their tricks to break down his story of American friendship.

In 1853 Commodore Perry, with four warships and 560 men, anchored in Yedo Bay with demands for proper treatment of shipwrecked American mariners. In return he promised friendship and trade. The Japanese tried to board the black ships and remove their guns and rudders. But American seamen drove them back. The Shogun tried to delay while he found some way to destroy these foreign devils. But Perry, suspecting treachery, said he had no time to waste in talk. He was weighing anchor. But he would return the following spring.

The Shogun sent for the Dutch traders and ordered them to build bigger ships than the American ones. They sent agents to Europe to buy guns, ammunition, and works on fighting with these weapons. Soldiers were drafted. Manjiro was ordered to the palace.

How had these foreigners been able to guide their enormous ships across the tractless seas, the Shogun demanded. How had they been able to find Japan?

Manjiro showed them his massive copy of Bowditch's *Navigator*.

"In this book," he said, "is all the knowledge that will enable men to find their way across oceans. It is no magic but knowledge such as the Americans have had for many years. By this book they travel all over the world, to places such as the Japanese have never known."

Did he understand that book? Could he teach this knowledge to others?

The answer was Yes.

Manjiro was taken from the prison and scholars were appointed to help him translate the monumental work into Japanese. Twelve translations were made, each one copied by hand. They became the most studied works in Japan. Today some of them remain and are still prized in Japan's leading universities. The instruments were imitated as accurately as possible, and even Manjiro's whaleboat was taken to pieces and each piece copied, even to the tool marks. Fifty Gloucester-built whaleboats were the beginning of what was to be the greatest navy in the world.

"But," Manjiro insisted, "the Americans come in peace. However, they are not foolish, nor are they meek. If you make them fight, they will bring ships larger than those black ships you have seen and they will blast our towns from the earth. Yet they are kindly people. Be their friends!"

"The traders of Deshima say they have come to destroy us!"

"The American words are peaceful," Manjiro insisted. "The traders do not want to share their trade with others. Perhaps they twist those peaceful words in translating them."

But the Shogun still was preparing for war when Commodore Perry returned with ten ships and two thousand men. He also brought such wonderful gifts as American clothing, tools, toys, a glittering sewing machine, and steam engines.

Manjiro Nakahama

Captain William H. Whitfield

The Samurai Sword

When the Americans gathered in the great audience chamber with the Japanese and their Dutch and Chinese interpreters, they did not know that, sitting behind a screen and listening carefully to the translations, was the man who had once been cabin boy of the whaleship *John Howland* of New Bedford, Mungo John.

Through him the Shogun received a true account of the American propositions. As a result the Japanese promised hospitality to all Americans who cared to land on Japanese soil. U.S. ships were permitted anchorage, and American coal could be placed at their disposition in Japanese ports. Delighted and surprised, for they had expected resistance, Commodore Perry and his staff returned triumphantly to the United States.

Within a few years Japan's closed door was open for the first time in three centuries. The shogunate was abolished, and the Emperor took over command. Foreign diplomats came to live in Japan and Japanese officials visited the world capitals, making treaties wherever possible.

Manjiro Nakahama was appointed to teach navigation in Japanese colleges. He became a professor of Tokyo University. In 1860, Manjiro was a senior officer aboard the first Japanese battleship to enter a United States port. In 1870 he was received by the President in Washington. He took the opportunity to call upon his old friend and benefactor, Captain Whitfield, now retired to Fairhaven, and to visit the schools he had attended in New Bedford.

Later he married and made a fortune in what was to become one of Japan's biggest industries, whaling, of course. Manjiro Nakahama died in 1898.

Twenty years later, his eldest son, Toichiro Nakahama, a prominent doctor in Tokyo, was proud to show his appreciation of Captain Whitfield's kindness to his father.

On July 4, 1918, the Japanese ambassador to the United States presented to the town of Fairhaven, at a meeting presided over by Lieutenant-Governor Calvin Coolidge, a Samurai sword of fourteenth-century workmanship, to commemorate the rescue of Manjiro Nakahama by Captain William H. Whitfield, "Out of whose kindness friendly relations between the people of Japan and the people of America were encouraged and made possible."

VI.

WE FIND AMBERGRIS

Mad Tony Sloan and the Zanzibar smugglers . . .
Kidnapped . . . Tony's escape.

WE WERE CRUISING the Carroll Grounds, between Ascension Island and the African Coast. The air was so clear, you could see for a hundred miles, and the southeast trade wind kept us on long heeling tacks as we zigzagged over the ocean. We took four sperm out of a big pod, tried them out, and had gone almost a week without raising spouts. I was still first lookout with Jimmy Leeds, the wind blowing our shirts off as we scanned the glittering seas. I caught a thin spout to windward.

"Blo-o-o-ws!" I called. "Blo-o-ws." Pleased I was to be the only one to sing out.

"Where away?" Captain Shockley cried from the deck far below.

"To larboard, sir. Headed south!"

"Belay!" Leeds shouted from beside me. "Right whale."

Captain Shockley said something I couldn't hear. But from the helmsman's laughter I knew it was no compliment.

"Look," I grumbled to Leeds. "You said right whales don't come into warm waters. Besides, that spout is two miles off. How d'you know it's a right whale?"

"Keep your eyes open, and your mouth shut, and listen," Leeds said. "Maybe you'll learn something. What d'you know of a whale's spout?"

"It isn't water, I know that. It's warm air that comes out, mixed with spray so it looks like water instead of vapor."

"What else?"

"A sperm spout slants for'ard. But that one's too far off to tell."

"Put your glass on it and you'll see that spout goes straight up. So it ain't a sperm. That makes it a right whale. Now take another look and see what kind of right whale it is."

I waited for the next rising and made out the spout again. But it seemed to be double.

" 'Tis," Leeds said. "All whales have double spout holes save only the sperm. How high d'you figure that spout?"

"Can't tell. Twenty feet, maybe."

"So. That makes it a right or a bowhead. Sulphur bottoms and finbacks spout fifty feet. It can't be a bowhead because there ain't no bowheads in these waters. So it's a right whale. Know why we call them right whales?"

I began to feel ashamed of all the things I didn't know.

"First time whalemen killed one, they found he had thicker blubber and more baleen than any other kind. So he was 'right.' Savvy? The rest has less blubber and less bone but they're the same general shape, so they still call them right whales. You figure you can remember all that?"

I said I hoped so.

"Want to know how to tell the size of a sperm whale?"

"At two miles off?" I scoffed.

"Four if ye like. A sperm whale, when he sounds to

feed, stays down a minute for every foot of his length. And when he breaches, he spouts once for every minute he stays down; that's if he ain't gallied or scared. So all you have to do is count the spouts and you know how big he is."

I promised to write it all down when I went below. But before we were relieved I raised a spout that proved Leeds wrong.

It was less than a mile from the ship, a for'ard slanting spout and not very strong. He spouted twice and turned flukes; we slid down the backstay to our boat.

"Looks like we got a two-foot whale." I laughed at Leeds.

"Sonny," he puffed while we were lowering. "Unless I miss my guess, we got something whalemen don't see much more'n once in a lifetime."

"Appears a mite poorly," Mr. Nanton said as we rowed. "Look at that spout; feeble and dirty. Peak your oars, lads, and out paddles."

We turned about on our thwarts. We were to leeward of him. He wasn't far off, and the wind brought down a stink that was worse than a save-all cask. Leeds, in the bow, signaled us to come up on his right side. He was going ahead, slow, his head out and his eye above water. We paddled over the tip of his fluke and the blubber was wrinkled, covered with sea lice, the black skin rubbed off in great whitish patches. There were circular scars from squid all over him.

"Old bull," Mr. Nanton muttered. "Too sick to cruise with the pod. Keep astern of his eye, Jimmy; he may be a bad 'un. Now. Give it him!"

Leeds darted his number one iron, snatched the spare, and buried it to the hitches abaft the fin. The flukes rose and half-heartedly slapped the sea, and the head lifted as he surged forward. Then he humped his back and sounded. Nanton changed ends with Leeds and we hauled up to him

as he breached a little way ahead. Then we bowed in and
Mr. Nanton lanced him for'ard of his hump.

He rolled feebly, chopping with his underjaw, then tried
to pitchpole, turning, as he bobbed, to get his eyes on whatever was tormenting him. But the lance had done its work.
He spouted, pink, then black clots of blood that rolled down
his forehead. He lashed the sea, throwing up great chunks
of evil-smelling food. Then he started off in a wide circle,
beating the water feebly until he turned on his side and
slowed down.

"Fin out!" Olaf spat. "My, he stinks!"

"Get a line about his flukes," Mr. Nanton ordered. "We
don't want to lose this one."

The *Canton* was running down to us as the Third Mate's
boat pulled alongside.

"Scoop up that gurry," Mr. Nanton told them, pointing
at the greasy lumps of matter in the bloodstained water.
"Lively, now!"

The *Canton* backed her yards and we hauled alongside
and made our whale fast under the stage. Already long blue
sharks were finning back and forth, waiting for us to cut.

Captain Shockley made the head cuts and Mr. Nanton
started the scarf. It came up thin, brow-flecked, and rotten.
The deck crew looked overside, gagging in the awful smell.

"He ain't got enough oil to grease the trypots," the cooper
grumbled.

"He's got something else though, shouldn't wonder."
Leeds winked at me.

"Pass a half-round spade over here," Captain Shockley
called, "and keep these sharks off me."

The whale was turned on his back while a head-tackle
was rigged. Captain Shockley, a monkey rope about him, was
lowered on to the small of the animal. He started digging at

the vent while sharks slid up almost to his feet before I chopped them with my spade. He probed inside the creature, fetching out lumps of putrid matter that a hand carefully scooped up and dumped in a tub. Meanwhile the underjaw was taken aboard and the case lifted on deck for bailing. Then the whale was cut adrift and left to float downwind, followed by a wriggling school of sharks that didn't seem to mind the stink at all.

"Know what that stuff is?" Leeds said when we went aboard. "Ambergris!"

A load of ambergris

Captain Shockley was washing it in sea water, carefully examining each horrible piece and either breaking it up or throwing it overboard. It was black, veined with what looked like white fat. It was more like dirty beeswax than anything I ever saw. The Captain broke several pieces of hornlike material from it.

"Squid beaks," Leeds told me. "That's what made him sick. Stuff forms to heal over the cuts them beaks made in his innards. Looks like it plugged him up."

I picked up a bit of the waxy stuff. Clean, it had a very

faint half-sweet smell, like fresh earth after rain. When it
was separated from the gurry, Captain Shockley sent for the
scales. All hands watched intently while he weighed it.

"Nine pounds," he said. "Worth maybe two hundred
and fifty dollars a pound."

I was glad when the case was bailed and the ship free of
that stench of rottenness. Captain Shockley called for jars
and carefully corked the ambergris down to keep its strength.
All hands were talking about the mysterious stuff—how the
Oriental people make it into incense, medicine, and how we
use it for perfume.

"I've seen little bottles in Port Said," Owen told us.
"Looks like ordinary tallow. But it's scented with attar of
roses. Costs five dollars or so an ounce. No wonder the
stuff's so expensive!"

"What sort of medicine do they use it for?" I asked.

"Never you mind," Owen said sharply. "You'll find out
soon enough. But them Eastern princes pay better than the
Ambergris King, back in Provincetown. I remember, back
in the old *Athlete,* taking thirty pounds of ambergris from
a sperm off Zanzibar. Used to be good grounds in those
days, but it's all fished out now."

"What about the ambergris and the prince?" one of the
Third Mate's crew demanded.

Owen waited for us to settle down before starting his yarn.
And not until we were almost begging him would he begin.

Captain didn't know what to do with thirty pounds of
ambergris. We were a long time from home, all hands broke,
in need of a run ashore and some spending money. So he
decided to put in at Zanzibar and see if one of those Arab
merchants wouldn't give him a fair price for the ambergris.

We dropped anchor some two miles offshore and set

double watches on the boats. Zanzibar was a bad place in those days. Most of the Zanzibaris were slavers; ran dhows up to the Red Sea and across to the Persian Gulf right under the noses of the British slave patrol boats. And there were whispers that they weren't too particular who they kidnaped and sold.

Anyway, Captain put on his best clothes and went ashore to call on the British consul. He told him about the ambergris and said he was looking for a buyer. The consul said he'd see what could be done.

Outside, Captain found his boat crew surrounded by screaming Arabs and Swahilis, all begging and trying to sell them things. They followed them to the boat, still screeching and cursing. But there was no trouble.

That night one of the lookouts sang out that two boatloads of natives were coming alongside.

"Tell 'em to stand off," the Captain shouted. "Light the cressets!"

Smoky flames lit up the whole ship and two large boats filled with people in white gowns. Captain let them see the shotgun under his arm and signaled one boat to come alongside. The paddlers brought her in and a big fat fellow stood up in the stern. He had a bright silk turban and a plumcolored gown over a white shirt. On his belt was a big curved dagger, made of silver by the look of it. His face was the shape of a ham—yellow, with big sad eyes, a hooked nose, and a curly beard. He waved fat hands with rings on every finger. A thin man in a dirty gown and fez stood up with him. He looked like a pickpocket.

"Me, savvy Inglesi, Cap'in," he squeaked. "Master want ambar."

"I got thirty pound," the Captain said. "What'll he pay?"

"*Shufti*. Make see."

"Let them two on board, Mister," Captain said. "And break out the ambergris."

The fat one knelt beside the open keg, his moon face close to it. He smelled it, touched it, rubbed it between his fingers, moaned, made little whining sounds, and carried on like he wanted to cry.

"Tahib," he mumbled. "Very good."

"How much for thirty pound?"

"He say fi' thousand Zanzibar dollar."

"Ten thousand," Captain said.

The fat one screamed like he'd been stuck.

"He poor man," the interpreter whined. "He pay six thousand."

"Nothing doing."

"Mister Cap'in. You pay me hundred dollar. I tell him pay eight thousand."

"You scummy little rat. You tell your boss I want nine thousand and not a piaster for you."

The two went to the rail and whispered, peering at us over their shoulders like they were afraid we'd knife them.

"Eight thousand dollar."

"Cash?"

"Aiwa."

"Let's see it."

"Weigh ambar."

With a lot of yelling, scales were passed up from one of the boats.

"He say twenty-nine pound."

"I don't care what it is," Captain shouted. "If you want that there ambergris the price is eight thousand dollars, cash."

There was more whispering and spreading of hands. Then,

sighing like his heart broke, the fat one agreed. The ambergris was put back in the keg, it was headed, and he dropped sealing wax on it. Then the interpreter picked it up.

"Belay that," Captain said. "Where's the cash?"

"Bring tomorrow."

"Listen, you hooky-nosed rapscallion. No cash, no ambergris. C.O.D. Savvy?"

They crouched on deck, calling out to their friends in the boats, cussing each other, and begging the Captain. Finally the interpreter said that if his boss brought that much money through the town, the authorities would spot it and confiscate it for back taxes he owed.

"No skin off my nose," Captain said. "You bring the cash if you want this here stuff."

They argued until morning. Finally the Captain agreed to take the keg to the dhow basin, where the big Indian Ocean vessels wait for the southwest monsoon, the following night and wait for a signal; a lantern lifted and lowered three times. He was to reply with the same signal. Then they'd hand over the silver and collect the ambergris.

Soon as it was dark, they lowered the keg into the Captain's boat and pulled away. Stroke oar was Tony Sloan, a husky lad of sixteen. They pulled past the town, listening to the plunk of guitars and the whining songs those people sing. They found the two moles that guard the basin, slid between them, and rested on their oars.

It was black as a whale's insides in that basin—no stars, no moon, nothing. All they could hear was the lap of water against the boat and the tinkle of a watchman's mouth harp aboard one of the dhows, lying on her bilge in the mud.

"Keep your eyes open," Captain said softly. "I don't like this quiet."

For a couple of hours they waited. Once they heard someone crying out in the distance and then there was the quiet splash of paddles.

"Back to the ship," Captain said suddenly.

The boat swung about and they pulled for the narrow passage between the moles. Something loomed up across their bow.

"Ahoy," Captain shouted. "Boat ahoy. Sheer off."

There was a low shout and the boat bumped them. Cloaked figures swarmed aboard swinging clubs. Their craft rocked, half swamped, as Arabs, squealing like pigs, laid about them. The Captain fired a pistol, and Tony saw a half-naked black lift the keg and heave it into the other boat. He yelled and dived after it. He was trying to get the keg back when something hit him over the head and he went out like a light.

Next thing Tony knew he was in a sort of shed that smelled of spices. He was tied hand and foot and a rag was twisted between his jaws. Sunlight speared down through holes in the mat roof. He tried to shout and almost strangled. Then he rolled and kicked madly against the wall. The door opened and a big Swahili in a loincloth and little cap looked in. Tony tried to talk and he loosed the gag.

"Water," Tony whispered. "Gimme some water, you ugly heathen!"

The man went out and came back with a spouted brass pot. Tony took a pull of tepid water and felt better.

"Now let me up," he said, "and I'll knock them pointed teeth out of your ugly mug."

The man put his heel in Tony's face and shoved. Tony went flat. The man spat on him and went out.

Tony lay there so mad he could hardly breathe. Another native came in with a dab of peanut paste and a handful of white manioc on a banana leaf. He loosed Tony's arms, and he ate, well as he could, for his sore mouth. Then they brought some more water, tied him up again, and left him.

Tony lay there wondering what on earth they were going to do with him. Had they got away with the ambergris, and what had happened to the Captain and the rest of the boat crew? He recognized the spicy smell in that shed. He knew he must be somewhere outside the town on one of the clove plantations.

But why? Suppose they'd killed the others, they surely wouldn't let Tony go to get the police after them. Maybe they'd kill him, too. But they'd have done that already if they intended to. The only thing he could figure was that they planned to sell him as a slave, and that scared the daylights out of him.

He struggled wildly with the coconut fiber ropes that bound him. They rasped the hide off wrists and ankles, but he couldn't loose the knots. He tried to yell. But they'd never have left the gag off if there was anyone to hear him. He rested and had another go at freeing his hands. But the knots seemed to get harder as his wrists swelled. In the evening they brought more food, and when they tied him again, the ropes were even tighter. But he had spotted the edge of a broken pot sticking out of the hard-packed dirt floor. He rolled to it and started sawing back and forth. He could hear them singing outside, and the flicker of firelight came through cracks in the wall. He worked until sweat rolled off him, his mouth dry with fright. At last the ropes gave and he sat up, nursing his bloody wrists. He was trying to loose his feet when someone opened the door. He lay back and pretended to be asleep. Whoever it was spat on him and went out.

Soon as the man left, Tony got the ropes off his ankles and sat rubbing them to get the stiffness out. Then he took a look through one of the cracks. There were several sheds, and outside them a fire with half a dozen Arabs sitting around it, eating out of a pot. Tony guessed they'd be armed. They'd either shoot him or pull him down like hounds if he tried to run for it. He studied the outside and thought he saw a path between clove trees beyond the fire. Maybe that led to a road. But how to get there? He couldn't reach it without being seen.

Then he remembered something he'd read somewhere; about how Moslems are afraid of mad people. They think crazy folk are afflicted by their god, Allah. It was his only chance.

He crouched beside the door and started making sounds. First he laughed. The Arabs yelled something at him. He grunted like a pig; Moslems think pigs are unclean. Then he began to sing; all the songs he knew, then the hymns. He screamed, whistled, sobbed, and laughed some more. At last someone started for the door. Quick as a flash, Tony slipped off his pants and shirt and when the door opened, he jumped for it.

"Hiyiyiyiyiyiyi!" he screamed.

The Arab jumped back with a yell, and Tony ran out into the firelight, naked as a jaybird. One of the Arabs snatched up a cutlass. Tony danced away from that and capered around, waving his arms, snapping his fingers, and yelling at the top of his voice.

The Arabs crowded to the other side of the fire, watching him uneasily. He laughed at them, made faces and cocked snooks. Then he jumped right into the fire and out the other side. That did it. They bolted, howling, into the darkness.

Still carrying on, Tony ran back to the hut, brushed cinders off his scorched feet, and got into his clothes. Then he picked up the cutlass that Arab had dropped and ducked into the dark path.

At the end of it was a gate. A watchman crouched, half asleep in the dirt. Tony let him have the flat of the cutlass across the head, climbed the gate and found himself in a road. It was on a hill; there were lights below, then the sea, and he made out what he thought was the *Athlete*. At least he knew which way to run.

Tucking his head down, he started trotting. Once a figure came out of a doorway, slinking sideways at him like a wolf. He ran at it, yelling, the cutlass glittering as he swung it. The stranger ducked back and bolted.

Tony hurried down a narrow twisting hill. There were dark shops, narrow cobbled streets with high sidewalks. Then he heard shouted orders and a low moaning. He crouched behind a stone post and saw Arabs with whips herding a long line of naked slaves. They were chained neck and neck, their hands free to carry bundles, their ankles fettered. They moaned sadly as their masters poked and whipped them like they were animals. Tony watched, his heart in his mouth. If those slavers got him! He waited until they were gone and stole along the narrow street, ducking into doorways at every sign of movement.

It was almost daylight when he came out into a square with a fountain in it. To one side were nodding palms, and beyond them, the sea.

Tony ran to the sea wall. About two miles offshore the *Athlete* rode at anchor. Shouting wildly, he raced along the Marina looking for a boat. He stopped to rest, and a gang of soldiers in red trousers and fezzes surrounded him. Tony backed against the wall, cutlass ready.

"Go ahead," he said softly. "Come on. You ain't taking me for a slave."

One of the soldiers yelled something and stepped close. Tony swiped at him. He jumped back, yelling. Another leveled a wide-bored musket. Tony watched him, his insides aching. He was about to risk a charge when someone collared him from behind. The soldiers swarmed all over him, and he was hauled to his feet, struggling wildly. A mob of people gathered, screeching and laughing as the soldiers dragged him into a narrow street. They stopped at a barred archway. Behind the bars was a court in which squatted dozens of natives, some naked, some with dried blood clotted on their faces. One, foaming at the mouth and sitting apart from the rest, was in chains.

"You ain't putting me in there," Tony panted.

But a soldier struck at the bars and the prisoner shrank back while another unlocked an enormous padlock. Tony dug in his heels as they shoved at him. But they threw him inside and locked the barred gate. Tony clung to it, the prisoners crawling about his legs like wolves. He yelled and shouted, then knelt down and said his prayers.

After he got up, he pushed through the foul-smelling prisoners to the bars again. Outside, Arabs strolled languidly hand in hand. Once or twice he saw white men in the distance, but every time he hailed them the prisoners set up such howls that no one could hear him.

"They can't leave me here," he whispered.

At dusk a guard came with a calabash of food. The prisoners dived at it like sharks and crouched back, gobbling their portions and grinning at Tony.

Darkness came. Some slept, others whined and quarreled in corners. Tony kept his place, watching the dark street. He was hanging to the bars half asleep when he heard boot heels on the street.

"Help!" he shouted. "American in here. Help!"

The steps slowed, halted, and came close.

"What is it?"

"Mister, I don't know who you are. But get word to the *Athlete,* will you? American ship at anchor. I'm a prisoner here. Call my captain, please sir."

The man went away. It was midnight before soldiers came with a lantern and beat the others back while Tony stepped out into the street.

"Where's my ship?"

"Not so fast, young fellow," a bored voice said. "You're under arrest for attacking the Sultan's police."

"Where you taking me?"

"British consul."

"Good, he knows my captain."

The consul wasn't too pleased at being called to his office at that time of night. Tony told his tale and another man listened.

"Not much we can do, I'm afraid, unless you can identify the people who abducted you. We'll put you aboard your ship meanwhile."

A smart gig rowed him in style to the *Athlete,* and it was some time before the lookout would let him aboard.

He told the Captain his story, and they went ashore next morning to the consulate.

"Four of us got knocked about," the Captain reported, "and the ambergris was stolen by the same thieves who took this boy."

The consul promised to do what he could. But they never saw the ambergris or the fat, scented man who had stolen it.

So the *Athlete* put to sea with all hands grumbling. But, as the Captain said, they could think themselves lucky they weren't all sold into slavery like Tony almost was.

VII.

I LEARN HARPOONING

. . . and harpoon a porpoise . . . John Boyle
O'Reilly's escape . . . The cruise of the Catalpa.

WE SENT HOME 350 barrels of oil from Cape Town and were headed across the South Atlantic toward the Patagonia Grounds. For this was a sperm cruise. Weather was good, the trades blowing steady day after day.

One morning Mr. Nanton put me to darting practice.

"Captain wants you to know all sides of the whaling trade," he told me. "You're husky enough to pull an oar and you've got whaling in your blood. So might's well get your bearings as a boat steerer."

I was mighty proud my uncle wanted to promote me, though I got a few sneers from Nelson. I knew I'd have to teach that townie manners before long.

The boat steerers now let me into their mess in the steerage and let me mount my own irons. We used single-flued harpoons, meaning the barbs were on one side only. They were called Temple toggle irons because they were invented by a Negro whalecraft maker named Lewis Temple in New

Bedford back in 1842. The steel head, seven inches long, had a sharp point and both barbs honed to cutting edges. This was fitted to a soft iron shaft so that it could pivot at right angles to the shaft under the pull of the whale, and thus hold. A wooden pin the size of a match, driven through holes in the head and the shank, held it parallel to the shank until it was driven into the whale. Then the pull broke the pin and the head turned at right angles, or toggled, making an anchor that held the boat fast to the whale until the boat header could get close enough to lance him. The harpoon was mounted on a six-foot oak or hickory shaft with the bark still on, to give the boat steerer a good grip. A round turn of line was spliced around the shank of the iron, stretched and tied in two places to the pole. At the end was an eyesplice or loop to which the whale line was bent.

This weapon was about ten foot over all, too heavy to be thrown like a spear. I learned to balance it, left hand halfway down the pole, my right at the end so I could sight down the pole and the soft iron shaft. The weapon was heaved with a final push by the right hand. Fifty feet was a good dart.

I practiced from the cutting-in stage on floating weed, jetsam from the ship; sometimes we lowered and I had to dart at floating casks. And let me tell you, to dart an iron fifty feet, often pitchpoling it, throwing it up in the air until the weight of the head pulled it downward—which you have to do if a whale is settling or you can't see over the crest of a wave—is mighty hard work. It wasn't often I could hit the cask that way; and every night my arms and back ached so I could hardly move until Jimmy Leeds gave me a rubdown with head oil.

Then one morning we ran into a school of porpoise rolling, breaching, and sporting about the bows.

"Hands could do with some fresh meat," Captain Shock-ley said. "Get down on the martingale stay and see can you iron a porpuss."

I went for'ard and took a look at the stay. It ran from beside the forefoot to the dolphin striker, the spar that runs down at right angles to the bowsprit, to strengthen it. I also noticed that at every pitch the dolphin striker stabbed down into the water. For a minute I wished it really would strike a dolphin and save me the trouble.

But Leeds passed a monkey rope around my waist and made it fast to the bow rail. Those of the watch not on duty crowded to watch me. I climbed down and at once was waist deep in the sea. But I held on, gasping for breath, to get my bearings.

The bow was like a big black wall, smelling of tar and streaming with water. I realized for a second that if I slipped, the vessel might well run me down. But I felt Leeds take up the slack in my monkey rope, so called for the iron.

They passed it down. I had to hang on with one hand, which meant holding that ten-foot harpoon with the other. I got it somehow and slid out on the stay, clinging tight as I could with my left hand.

A porpoise came surging up from under the ship, breached not a foot from my foot. I hauled back to dart at him but the vessel plunged just then and buried me in the bow wave. I held on, choking, and heard the hands laughing above and behind me. I'd let go my harpoon. Sheepishly I hauled it back and took another grip. This time I felt more secure. I'd been buried in the sea and nothing had happened. I had faith in Leeds, so I took another hold with my left hand and waited until the bow should rise and give me a good dart. I waited a long time, plunging down, rising up, until I began to feel a bit peculiar with this unfamiliar motion.

Then in the blue depths, maybe twenty feet ahead of the ship, I saw two big porpoise coming up to breathe. They were black, changing to gray as they neared the surface. I hauled back. One appeared, breached, and sounded with a twist before I could aim. The other, close by, came clear of the water. The bow was plunging downward. I darted, letting the ship do most of the work. I saw the head hit the blue-gray curve of his back and sink in. He broke his dive, skidding to one side as the heavy shaft bore him down.

"Fast oh!" I heard Leeds yell as I clambered, mighty quick, I can tell you, back to the deck. We hauled him in, still kicking. He was over seven feet long, and that night we ate porpoise steaks, which were tough but good. Next day cookie made meat balls with hardtack, dried onions we had picked up in Cape Town, and some flour. They were mighty tasty.

"Next lowering, you go as boat steerer," Mr. Nanton promised me.

I wasn't moved to the steerage yet, for until I had lowered as boat steerer, I was a foremast hand. My fo'c'sle mates took it well. Olaf said he'd be proud to pull tub oar for me, and Owen promised to keep my line flaked down sweet as milk. Pete Brava winked and nodded with a grin right across his dark face. I felt a bit funny about taking Jimmy Leeds's place; he'd been closer to me than anyone.

"Don't fret, young fellow," he said. "I'll be heading the Captain's boat, so it's promotion all around. 'Tain't often a hand makes boat steerer on his greenie cruise. You'll have your name in the *Mercury* when we finish the cruise."

"In the Boston *Pilot,* too," Owen said. "Editor's a friend of mine."

"Yeah, you knows everybody," Nelson sneered. "How come a fo'c'sle lush like you is pals with a editor?"

He was up through the scuttle and on deck before Owen could grab him.

"I was shipmates with him once," Owen said when he sat down again. "He wasn't always an editor. He was a soldier once, and a revolutionary. He also wrote poems and books. He'd been a convict, too. John Boyle O'Reilly is his name." And Owen settled himself to spin another yarn—a true one.

John Boyle O'Reilly was a schoolmaster's son, born near Drogheda, Ireland, in 1844. When he left school, he learned the printing trade, was a reporter, too. From the beginning he wanted to free his country from British rule, and when the Irish Republican Brotherhood was formed in the United States in 1858, he was one of the first to join.

He was only nineteen when he enlisted in the 10th Hussars. But not to serve the Queen. He was a secret agent of the Brotherhood, sworn to get as many troopers as possible to desert and join the Republican forces.

He was a likely lad in his tight blue uniform, of middle height, dark haired, with cheerful blue eyes. He was a good horseman and open-handed when treating his mates. It wasn't long before he was the most popular trooper in the squadron. He had about fifty ready to desert when someone informed and the lot of them were arrested and court-martialed. O'Reilly and five others were sentenced to be shot.

For a while it looked as though old man Death would put a stop to soldiering and the grand conspiracy too. They threw him in a Dublin jail. He escaped. They transferred him to a prison in England and he escaped again. Three times he escaped and was caught. Until, in 1866, his sentence was commuted to twenty years' penal servitude. That meant the horror of transportation.

In those days England sent her convicts to Australia. It

was far away, and chances were they'd never come back. Also, it saved the cost of prisons in England and provided labor for those who cared to hire it in the new colony.

In 1867 O'Reilly and the other Irish political prisoners were lock-stepped aboard the *Hugomont,* an ancient trooper now used as a prison ship, carrying hundreds of thieves, murderers, debtors, poor folk who had stolen a four-bit petticoat: men, women, and their children. They were packed into shelf bunks in the 'tween decks with eighteen inches of headroom and no light but that which filtered through deck gratings.

The food was the worst and cheapest that could be saved from the pigs, and they died like insects on that horrible eight-month voyage. And those who died, some said, were lucky! They had just one hour on deck every day to get as much fresh air as they could. By night they lay naked in sweltering heat, half suffocated in the stench of lime, sweat, and filth. Each morning the dead were dragged out and thrown to the sharks that convoyed the creaking ship across the tropical sea.

Eventually the shabby vessel dropped anchor at Bunbury, Western Australia. The exhausted prisoners stumbled ashore under the curious and pitiless eyes of freemen and their convict slaves. At once the new arrivals were assigned to camps and herded off by guards who, not so long before, had been convicts themselves; for only the most brutal would guard the convict settlements. In some camps gags, bridles, and headstalls were used on the convicts. At Norfolk, it was said, they still used the "stretcher." That was an iron frame six feet long by three wide. Victims were strapped to it with their hands hanging over the end. One, left for several hours, was dead when they loosed him. Some unruly prisoners were hung by a wrist for hours. Men were lashed until their backs were streaming blood. Then they were put to work in the cayenne pepper mills, where the very air itself was filled with agony.

One camp master was famous for his cruelty. Two convict "scourgers" trotted beside his stirrups when he rode out to inspect the road-building gangs. For the slightest fault he ordered flogging, and yelled with laughter while his jackals lashed the helpless convicts and rubbed salt into their wounds.

One day several of his convicts escaped and lay in ambush near the camp until the master rode by. They smashed in the heads of his scourgers and dragged him off his horse. He got up from the ground, glaring at their burned, haggard faces and their scarred bodies. He didn't laugh then. He offered them money, drink, even freedom if they'd only let him go.

"Oh, no, cully," their leader said, spitting through his broken teeth. "You hung me by the wrist once; you stretched my bunkie 'til he died. Look at our backs! You done that. Strip him!"

He screamed, begging for mercy, as they tore the clothing from his squirming, sweating body. Then they pegged him down on an ant heap. They smeared wild honey over his flabby belly and waited until the inch-long ants, black and vicious as stoats, began to cover him.

"Sleep well, cobber." They laughed, and went away.

When trackers came looking for him—and in no hurry—next day, they found a nicely polished skeleton.

For a while after that the camps were a torment. O'Reilly, though a political prisoner, was thrown in with the vilest criminals. But he got on with them. He backed down from no man, and they respected him for it. Many a time he got himself and his mates out of trouble with his quick wit, and the overseers found O'Reilly could do more than they could with the prisoners. So, after a few months he was made a "constable to aid the officers of the settlement." But he still had to wear boots with heavy nails arranged in a broad arrow so that he'd leave a convict track wherever he went. And if the officers of the settlement thought their constable would act as a sort of stool pigeon for them, they were mistaken. O'Reilly had other plans.

One day, carrying a message from one camp to another, he met Father McCabe, a parish priest of the settlement. He'd heard things of the Father, and so he decided to take a chance.

"They tell it you're a member of the Brotherhood, Father," he said, straight out.

"And what if I am?"

"If you are, you'll tell me how I can get away from here. For I'm of the Brotherhood, too. But I can't help the grand cause out here."

"Well, my son, if you try the bush, the snakes, the black fellows, or the bush rangers will get you. The only way is by sea. But bide yer time. I've friends and I'll see what's to be done."

O'Reilly went back to his camp. And for days he walked like a cat on hot bricks, waiting for word. Then one day a stranger, a freeman by his clothes, stopped him outside the camp.

"Name of Maguire," he said. "Father McCabe says there'll be an American whaleship in Geographe Bay. Now wait until you hear from me."

O'Reilly nearly went mad waiting. But it wasn't until February, 1869, that Maguire came again.

"The *Vigilant* of New Bedford, Captain Baker, will pick you up outside the bay. Tomorrow night slip your convict boots for these freeman brogans. Cut a false line to fox the trackers, then run over to the abandoned camp on the Vasse Road. Lie low 'til ye hear someone whistling 'St. Patrick's Day.' "

Next night O'Reilly stole through the gum bush, scurried like a dingo across the scrub desert, and lay silent as a weasel beside the old road. Insects crawled over him, and once something moved and hissed close to his face. He couldn't see, but he smelled the cold reek of a tiger snake. Like all Irishmen he hated the creeping things, and lay half fainting until the reptile went away. He was beginning to relax when the jackass birds suddenly fell silent and he heard the thud of hooves. There were soft voices, and he made out two shapes against the dark sky. Trackers? He flattened in the dust. Then he heard the faint skirl of "St. Patrick's Day" and jumped out and grabbed the bridle of Maguire's startled horse. The other man dismounted and passed his rein to O'Reilly.

"Boot and saddle," Maguire whispered. "Hup!"

They whirled off into the darkness. For hours they galloped until the horses plunged through rustling salt marsh and O'Reilly tasted the sea on his lips. The boom of surf was close and the foam a faint luminous glow when Maguire pulled up.

"Bide here," he said, " 'til I find the boat."

O'Reilly waited, gentling the panting horses, until a light blinked far down the beach. He rode to it and tethered the mounts. Maguire was pulling marsh grass off a boat.

"Gimme a hand," he said. "We'll make for South Cape. The *Vigilant* won't dare come inside Australian waters. We'll be able to sight her from the Cape and put off quick."

They shoved the boat into the water, rowing desperately through the heavy surf. All night they pulled, tossing in the empty bay.

"Haven't had bite nor sup for twenty-four hours," O'Reilly panted. "Have ye something to drink?"

"God help us," Maguire groaned. "I forgot the food."

They pulled on, tossing in heavy seas as the dawn wind freshened. The land was a brown blur far astern and the Cape not in sight. Wearily they rowed, and it was dark before they ran the surf and dragged the boat up the beach under South Cape. Then they staggered to a stream and gulped the sweet water. In a swamp Maguire found wild lilies.

"Black fellows make bread of these," he mumbled, chewing the raw bulbs. O'Reilly forced the sour stringy things down. They dragged cover over the boat and lay down to sleep.

O'Reilly was awakened by shouts. Maguire, tugging at the boat, pointed out to sea, where a sail was barely visible. They launched the boat, tumbled aboard, and pulled madly toward the distant vessel.

"Shout," Maguire panted. "She's changing course. Wave your shirt."

They stood up in the rocking craft shouting hopelessly as the *Vigilant* drew away and disappeared over the western horizon. Wearily they rowed back to the Cape.

"We're not done yet," Maguire said grimly. "There's an Englishman named Johnson has a cow camp down the beach. We'll have to trust him. I'll go ask him to bring you food, then I'll get back to Bunbury and see is another whaler due."

O'Reilly crawled under the boat and lay sheltered from the sun's heat. Evening came and a cold wind swept across the bay. Then he saw a young man, shotgun in one hand and a small package in the other. He crept fearfully along the beach, staring all around him. Then he dropped his package and bolted. O'Reilly ran out and sank his teeth thankfully into a heavy sandwich of beef and bread. Next day the man brought more food, always running for his life as soon as he dropped it.

Four days later Maguire arrived, followed closely by a hefty bruiser in ragged convict clothing.

"We've got passage for you aboard the whaleship *Gazelle*, Captain Gifford. This dirty rascal is a copper's nark. Followed me here like a mongrel dog. Says his name's Bowman."

The lout grinned and spat. "I goes along with ye or I peach. See?" He leered.

"Do we take him," Maguire asked, "or what?"

Bowman jumped back, a long thin skinning knife in his fist, his broken teeth bared wickedly. It was either take him or kill him, and neither of them had a taste for murder.

"Get the boat out," Maguire said. *"Gazelle's* off the bay right now."

They smashed through the surf and pulled far out, steering west, until in the late afternoon they sighted a sail to the north.

"Patrol boat," Bowman whined. "What'll we do?"

The vessel drew closer.

"Bark rigged," Maguire said, "and her sails are smoke-stained. She's the *Gazelle!"*

They toiled at the oars, gasping in the heat. Maguire stood up in the bow, waving his coat, until the whaleship backed her yards. In an hour they were alongside.

"Get me aboard," Bowman whispered, "or I blow the gaff!"

Mr. Hathaway, third mate of the *Gazelle,* looked down at the tossing boat.

"Which one of you is Mr. Brown?" he called.

"That's you!" Maguire shoved O'Reilly.

"Come aboard!"

Bowman squirmed after him, saluting like a beggar, his eyes darting about him like a rat looking for a hole.

"Take me, Guv'nor," he whined. "I'll work me passage. Mighty handy, I am. Willin' too. I'll do anythin'. Only don't send me back to them cruel overseers. Look what they done to my poor back."

"Get for'ard," Hathaway said. "You'll work, all right."

The whalemen cheered Maguire rowing back to land.

"Good luck, and thanks," O'Reilly called after him.

"Come aft," Hathaway said.

Captain Gifford looked up from his chart table. "Glad to have you," he said, shaking hands. "I'll give you passage far's Java. You'll bunk in the steerage."

"I'll work my way, sir, and thanks," O'Reilly said.

He fitted in quickly, insisted on taking his trick at the wheel and riding the mainmast hoops as the *Gazelle* rolled northward. But Bowman, now he felt secure, had become cock of the fo'c'sle. He cringed to the afterguard, but dodged work and flicked out his knife at every complaint.

"I was doin' time for murder," he told his mates. "I've killed better men than you scum, so I don't mind a few more. Cross me and I'll slit yer throats in yer sleep, I will."

By the time they reached Java, O'Reilly was popular with all hands.

"Stay with us if ye like," Captain Gifford said. "We can always use a good hand."

"Right you are, sir," O'Reilly said gratefully. "Anything to get me to America."

Two months from Geographe Bay, O'Reilly was pulling stroke oar in Mr. Hathaway's boat, as smart a whaleman as any aboard. The *Gazelle* put in at Rodriguez, a British island in the Indian Ocean, for water and fresh provisions. But no

sooner was the anchor down than a longboat with an officer
and a file of soldiers pulled alongside.

"We have information that you're carrying escaped prisoners," the officer stated. "You will muster all hands for in-
spection, please."

There was no time to hide. The crew stood along the rail
while the officer examined them, comparing them with the
descriptions he carried. One of the foremast hands earned
the everlasting gratitude of his mates by cocking a thumb at
Bowman.

"Take him," the officer ordered. O'Reilly, standing with
the officers, held his breath. But Bowman, a sly grin on
his face, climbed quietly into the boat and rowed ashore.

"Get water and food aboard quick's you can," Captain
Gifford ordered. "I want outta this port. Young feller, you
keep your weather eye lifted. That blackguard'll ship you
sure as shooting if it suits his book."

"Come with me, Johnny," Hathaway whispered.

He led O'Reilly to the cabin and lifted the hatch over
the space between deck and sternpost. It smelled of lime, tar,
oil, and mostly bilge.

"Lie down there. I'll come for you soon's we're off sound-
ings."

He ran on deck and sent off boats for food and water.
All that day he watched the shore. Then, just before dusk,
the longboat with the royal ensign trailing from her stern
came smartly out. Swiftly he ran aft, picked up the cooper's
grindstone, and heaved it into the sea.

"Man overboard," he bawled, ducking below. "Man overboard." He tossed a seaman's hat through an open port.
"Man overboard! Lower away!"

The crew were dashing about and boats slapping into the

sea as the Queen's longboat came alongside, Bowman grinning in the sternsheets.

"Man overboard!" Hathaway shouted. "Bear a hand there, sir. Man's drifted astern, I think."

The Queen's boat followed, her men searching the darkening sea. Hathaway leaned from his boat and scooped up the hat.

"No use," he said sadly. "He's gone. Back to the ship. Give way!"

"I'm looking for a man named Brown," the officer said when they were alongside.

"Brown?" Hathaway sighed. "That's the poor lad who went overboard!"

The grief of the crew, who really believed O'Reilly was drowned, fooled the officer. The *Gazelle* was allowed to put to sea. And not until then did Hathaway release the half-suffocated O'Reilly from his dank and smelly prison. You could have heard the *Gazelle* crew laughing all the way back to Rodriguez!

Their next landfall was the island of St. Helena.

"We transship our oil here," Captain Gifford told O'Reilly, "and go looking for more whales. Take these papers—belonged to John Soule, who deserted a year ago. They'll get you home quicker'n we can."

O'Reilly shook hands with every member of the *Gazelle's* crew, and that included Jimmy Owen. Then he shipped before the mast to Liverpool in the *Sapphire* packet. On the voyage he met a man named Bailey who helped him hide out in Liverpool until he was able to sign as third mate in the *Bombay*, Liverpool to Philadelphia. And on November 23, 1869, John Boyle O'Reilly was at last on free soil.

First thing he did was to take out naturalization papers. Then he got a job with a shipping firm. In his spare time

The bark CATALPA

he wrote poems and a novel, *Moondyne,* telling of his adventures in Australia. He met an American girl and married her. By 1875 he was editor and part owner of the Boston *Pilot.* He still kept in close touch with the Brotherhood, which was very active in the United States, for he had never forgotten his Irish mates in the Australian penal settlements.

With another Irishman, John Devoe, O'Reilly hatched the wildest plot of his life. It was to sail to Australia and rescue six important Irish political prisoners. His novel, which turned out to be a best seller, provided some of the money needed to buy a ship, the 200-ton whaling bark *Catalpa.* His old friend Hathaway of the *Gazelle,* now retired from the sea, helped him sign a crew under Captain Anthony of Nantucket, and the *Catalpa* sailed off on a roving charter in the hope of catching enough whales in Australian waters to pay for the real purpose of the expedition.

Meanwhile two agents, John Breslin, under the name of Collins, and Thomas Desmond, as Mr. Jones, were sent to Australia, posing as capitalists anxious to invest in the growing colony. They were received by the Governor and shown over everything, including the convict camps. Through a contact, William Foley, they were put in touch with James Wilson, who had been arrested with O'Reilly. They advised him of the six-man rescue plan. Wilson was to get the rest of them together and pass them through the guard lines to a meeting place where changes of clothing and transportation would be waiting.

Meanwhile the *Catalpa* reached Geographe Bay. But a government steamer and gunboat patrolling the bay kept a sharp eye on the Yankee whaler. It was on a rough night, off Rotten Nest Island, that the *Catalpa* was able to drop a boat without being seen and Captain Anthony, with five of his best men, pulled strongly for Rockingham, a village between Fremantle and Bunbury.

That same night Desmond and Breslin, driving buggies from different parts of town, met on the Rockingham Road. The prisoners were waiting in the scrub. Swiftly they threw off their convict rags and changed into the clothes the agents had brought. Then the two buggies drove through the darkness until a swinging light guided them to the whaleboat waiting on the beach.

They tumbled aboard and pulled straight out to sea. The *Catalpa* was not in sight. They set the lugsail, but an on-shore wind held them back all night, shipping water, bailing and shivering with cold.

"Sail ho," Anthony said as dawn broke. "The *Catalpa*." They stretched cramped legs and bailed some more.

Continued from Wednesday

At. 8 Am the Georgette fired a gun across our bow the Captian stood on the weather rail and raised his Speaking trumpet. the Georgette hailed back Ahoy the Captian Answered what do you want. Georgette then hailed heave to the Captian asked what for and again asked what am I to heave to for. After some time the georgette hailed have you any Convict. prisoners on board Captian no prisoners died again no prisoners that I no of Georgette then hailed I telegraph to you your thinnest do know that you are Amenable to British law in this Colony you have Six Convict. prisoners on board I See Some of them on deck now Captian Answered you are Mistake Sir the men you See are my Ship Crew georgette hailed Again I Give 15 minutes to Consider And you must take the Consequences I have the means to do it. And If you dont heave to I will blow the mast out of you the Captian Said I am on the high Seas that the American flag my flag protects me if you fire on this Ship you fire on the American flag Ship Continued her Course at. 8 30 wore Ship heading Sw. S georgette hailed again wont you Surrender held on our Course georgette hailed Again can I come on board Captian Answered no Sir I am bound to Sea and cant Stop at. 9 30 Am She left And we kept on our Course heading Sw So Ends this day

Sat.
Long.

The rescue of the prisoners is described in the log of
the CATALPA

"Strike that lug," Anthony snapped. "There's that danged steamer."

They lay, invisible to the steamer, in the breaking sea. But the gunboat was out too, and sighted them as the steamer made for shore.

"*Catalpa* ahoy!" Anthony bawled, standing up to wave his coat. "Row, you sons! Pull your backs out or that coast guard'll catch us."

The *Catalpa* change course toward them. The men rowed desperately, the prisoners standing up and yelling their heads off. The gunboat, under heavy sail, was nearing them when the *Catalpa* gibed and slid neatly between gunboat and whaleboat, plunging down on them like a battering ram.

"Stand by," the Mate howled from the bow of the *Catalpa*. "Steer small!"

They crouched in the smashing seas as the greasy hull surged past. Then snatched at the swinging fall blocks, hooked them at bow and stern, and were jerked high out of the water as hands tailed on to the boat-crane lines and hauled them aboard. They tumbled on deck, to be surrounded by cheering whalemen. But not for long. There was a report and a splash ahead.

"Gunboat *Georgette*, sir," the Mate reported. "Signalling us to heave to."

"Keep her as she goes, Mister," Captain Anthony said.

The *Georgette* drew abeam.

"You've six prisoners aboard," Colonel Hervest, troop commandant, megaphoned.

"No prisoners," Anthony replied.

"May we board you?"

"No, sir!" Anthony snapped.

"Beg to remind you, you're amenable to British law. Heave to or I'll sink you!"

"Run up our colors," Anthony ordered. "Serve out guns, lances, cuttin' spades, anything to fight with."

They could see red-coated soldiers on the *Georgette's* deck.

"Take cover under the bulwarks," Anthony said. "Now, quartermaster, head me straight on that vessel!"

The ponderous bows of the *Catalpa* rammed toward the gunboat.

"Heave to!" her captain shouted.

"Give way or I'll run ye down!" Anthony roared.

Amid the frantic slatting of sails, the *Georgette* backed her yards and the *Catalpa* surged past.

In August, 1876, she arrived safely in New York harbor.

The final dramatic touch delighted O'Reilly's heart. The Police Department of Western Australia sent a bulky package of documents to the Police Chief of New Bedford, Massachusetts, home port of the *Catalpa*, reporting the ship's part in the escape of the Fenian prisoners and demanding information as to their whereabouts. The Australian Police Chief might have received more information had the New Bedford Police Chief been anyone else but Hathaway, one-time third mate of the *Gazelle*, and one of the most active of the escape agents.

VIII.

CROSSING THE SOUTH ATLANTIC

Scrimshaw . . . I harpoon my first whale . . . Promoted to boat steerer . . . Gam with the Charles W. Morgan.

I'LL NEVER FORGET my first lowering as boat steerer. We'd run across the South Atlantic for three weeks without raising a spout. All hands, with nothing to do but stand watches, make and mend and man the yards when necessary, were at scrimshaw; planing pan bone, sawing sperm teeth, smoothing the surfaces with files or dried shark skin and drawing the lines to guide knife points and needles to the final proud designs.

No one seems to know how this spare-time work got the name scrimshaw. Some say it's an old Nantucket Indian word. Anyway, the first to practice it were the old colonial whalemen during the long waits between spouts. One thing certain is that scrimshaw is the only art, apart from Indian work, that is truly American.

The original scrimshaw was the engraved sperm tooth, with the lines cut by needles or knife points rubbed with a mixture of whale oil and soot from the tryworks and polished dry. The result looked like black-and-white etchings. Some were pictures of ships or the killing of whales. Some whalemen made etchings of their homes or patriotic scenes. Others made pinups. But they usually traced them from pictures in magazines; fine ladies in bustles and high collars and such. Some artists went in for sculpture. In the Old Dartmouth Historical Society Whaling Museum in New Bedford is a little statue group of a man kneeling to his sweetheart; the group is called "The Proposal of Marriage."

Some of our men were making stay busks of pan bone to fit in front of a lady's corset. They were about sixteen inches long and two wide, and decorated with love birds, clasped hands, and verses. Like these:

> "This bone once in a sperm whale's jaw did rest.
> Now 'tis intended for a woman's breast.
> This my love I do intend
> For you to wear and not to lend."

> "Accept, dear Girl, this busk from me;
> Carved by my humble hand.
> I took it from a sperm whale's jaw
> One thousand miles from land.
> In many a gale has been the Whale
> In which this bone did rest.
> His time is past, his bone at last,
> Must now support thy brest!"

But most of the hands were working on jagging wheels for crimping the edges of pies. It isn't surprising that a whaleman, who for a couple of years eats nothing but hardtack, salt horse, and on rare occasions boiled duff sweetened with blackstrap, dreams of the delicious pies he used to get at home.

Some were carved into horned beasts, the paws holding the wheel and the horn for piercing the crust. Some had two wheels of different patterns; some folded and had fretted handles inlaid with polished turtle shell. There were candlesticks, cribbage boards, pestles, mortars, napkin rings—all decorated with birds, fish, whales, stars, anchors, and bells. Some made chessmen, checkerboards, and little ditty boxes. Captain Shockley was making a swift to be used for winding silk or wool. It was a revolving cylinder, made to be clamped on the edge of a table. A beautiful thing, it was made of dozens of strips of pan bone connected, lattice fashion, with each other and the axis of the cylinder, so that the diameter could be made bigger or smaller.

Even Nelson was at it. He was carving a piece of pan bone into a blackjack shaped like a fist, and he had a set of bone knuckles decorated with stars.

The mates made bone canes worked to look like rope or bamboo, with handles of sperm teeth carved into sailor knots, swan necks, crowns, and birds' heads. I, as boat steerer, made some chock pins of bone and polished them until they looked like ivory.

Owen had a flat piece of bone on which he had made a drawing of the *Canton* with whales and boats all about her. It was a fine thing, and I wondered what he would do with it. For he was in a bad way. All his liquor was gone and he couldn't get any more. He begged the Captain, and even the cook, for lemon extract. So it was good he had the scrimshaw to work with; otherwise he would have been in trouble.

Then, one morning off the River Plate Grounds, the lookout raised spouts.

"Bloooooows!" he yelled. "Blows and breaches. Sparm!

"The Proposal of Marriage"

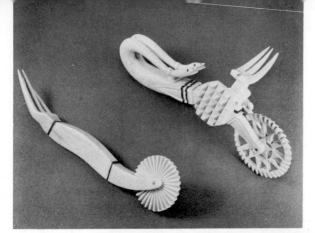

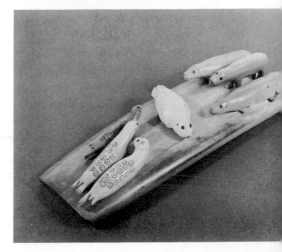

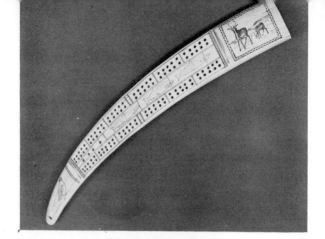

whaleman's art

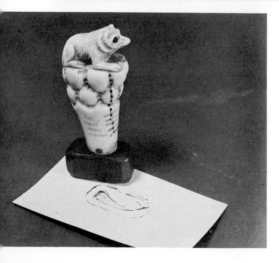

Sparm! Blooooows and white-waters! Sparm! All over the ocean!"

All four boats lowered, and we pulled toward a pod of twenty and more sperm. I was at harpooner's oar with Jimmy Leeds, whose place I had taken, backing me up at number one oar.

"Greasy luck, boy," he whispered. "Here's where you grease your iron!"

We hadn't far to pull; they were coming our way head and head.

"Paddles," Mr. Nanton said softly. "They're passaging. Peak them oars."

We turned about, and I got to my standing board in the bow, jamming my thigh in the clumsy cleat and shaking free the short warp of my number one iron.

Ahead a line of heads came plunging toward us like the bows of ships. They rose high, spouted, humped, and sounded, slow and terrible. Regular as clockwork they came, breaching twenty feet out of the water and slamming back, the ocean white with foam as far as we could see. And they were coming straight at us. I took a quick look about. Strung out in a line were the other three boats, and they seemed mighty frail with those battering rams surging down on them.

"Stand by, Lester," Mr. Nanton called.

I felt my hands go wet. I gripped my iron but I couldn't move. The great heads plunged closer.

"Stand by, sonny," Jimmy Leeds whispered.

I couldn't move. The whales were close. I could hear their spouts hissing like live steam and the smash of waves that creamed up over their snouts. One of them was headed straight at us.

"Stand by!"

Mr. Nanton steered us between two great whales. They smelled dank and oily, and the sea broke over us. I saw an eye small as a tennis ball look right at me through the froth as the whale humped.

"Give it him!" Nanton yelled.

I watched the blue-black side glide past and saw the squid scars and sea lice in the cracked black skin. Then the flukes lifted high above us and slid under, smooth as oil. We rocked in the oily wake. And I still gripped my iron.

"Take the iron, Leeds," Nanton snapped. "Number one oar, Mosher."

That shook me. I turned and saw the crew staring at me, sort of embarrassed.

"What sort of boat steerer d'you mean to be?" Nanton yelled, mad as a bear.

"Give him a chance, Mister Mate," Leeds said quietly. "First dart is a tough one. Remember?"

"All other boats fast," the Mate said bitterly. "And we didn't even dart. Cost your mates sixty barrels, that's what!"

I turned for'ard, ashamed to face them. I felt hot all over, and my face must have been red. My stomach was a hard knot; I felt helpless and not far from blubbering.

"Give way," the Mate said in disgust. "Maybe we can bear a hand to the others."

Then, "Blo-o-o-ws!" Jimmy Leeds yelled. "Blo-o-o-ws. Over yonder!"

Far astern of the whales a long spout sparkled in the sunshine.

"Give way," Nanton said. "Down from the bow, Mosher."

"Stay where you be," Jimmy Leeds whispered, and started pulling.

I pretended I hadn't heard the Mate, and he said no more.

The lone sperm was heading toward us. As he breached, I saw a great white slash across his snout.

"An old bull," Jimmy Leeds said. "Chased out of the pod by a younger one. But he's big! Reckon you were saving your iron for this one."

"Stand by," Nanton called softly.

I shipped my paddle and stood up. This time I hefted my iron and wondered if I'd be able to dart it. The bull came nearer, plunging down on us like a pitching ship—breaching, sounding, breaching, spouting.

"Next rising," Jimmy whispered.

"Stand by!"

The Mate swung the boat, and the head came up right beside us, the glistening side sliding past like a massive black wall. I heaved back, bracing my knee for purchase.

"Give it him!"

I darted that iron midway between eye fin and hump, snatched the spare, and buried it to the hitches.

"Fast—oh!" I yelled.

The whale sounded deep, his flukes slapping the sea with the sound of a cannon. We were yanked about like a chip, line running out until the loggerhead creaked. Then he breached ahead, half of him out of the water, and started running on the surface right toward the other boats and their whales.

We clung to the line, smashing through the sea in a real Nantucket sleigh ride. Our whale sounded as we passed the boats but kept our line taut. Then the ship was abeam, and we were still smashing through warm rollers. The whale sounded again.

"Change ends, Boat Steerer," Mr. Nanton called.

I danced over the thwarts, my feet dodging the murderous line, but I felt like the king of the world. I tumbled into the

A whaler about to harpoon a whale

stern sheets and snatched the steering sweep. Owen, flaking
down line like a machine, glanced up and winked at me.
Far ahead the whale breached, tossed flukes, and sounded
again. We ran over him.

"Haul away!" Nanton shouted.

All hands laid on the line while Nanton peered down into
the water under our keel. Next rising, the bull was only two
boat lengths ahead. We steered over his flukes and slid past
his hump.

"Bow me in!"

I heaved on the sweep. We veered, and our bow struck

solidly. Nanton rested the lance point against the streaming hide and leaned. The iron sank in five feet. Then he churned, jerking the pole up and down while the wicked little blade gashed the inside, searching for the blood vessels that would fill the whale's lungs and kill him. But the bull tossed flukes, throwing the lance high until its line brought it up short and it fell into the sea. Nanton snatched another. But the bull was rolling, "jawing back," as we say, smashing the sea with his underjaw that would have splintered us. I heaved on the sweep to steer clear, but Nanton bawled me to bow in. We slid close, not a man length from that snapping jaw, and Nanton lanced again.

"Stern all!"

The flukes smashed not a fathom from where I stood. We backed off, the lance in him. He rolled, the line wrapping itself about him, flukes lashing as we paid out line to prevent him from dragging us under.

"Bow me in again," Nanton panted, hauling in the first lance. It was bent; he jammed the shaft in a notch and kneed it straight. We slid in close to the maddened whale. Nanton eyed him coolly, picked his spot, and drove the lance, riding it until the whale gave a frightful convulsion, ejecting masses of half-digested food from his gaping mouth. Then he righted and tried to run. But he was spouting clear blood. Soon he circled in the death flurry and rolled, fin out, a hundred fathoms off. We pulled up to him, the crew scooping water to wash off his blood from their heads and shoulders. I clung to the steering sweep and stared at the immense floating mass. I shook all over and I prayed I wouldn't be sick. But all hands were grinning at me, Nanton included.

"Greasy luck." Owen chuckled, fishing for his pipe.

"Biggest sperm I ever clapped eyes on. He'll go eighty barrels, eh Mr. Mate?"

We secured four whales that day. Mine gave up 72 barrels of oil. His jaw was 19 feet long and he had 42 teeth. I still have one. I tried to scrimshaw it, but didn't get farther than pricking the outline of a lady's head on it.

I was moved to the steerage, for I was a real harpooner now, a boat steerer, and entitled to wear a chock pin in my buttonhole. But I still spent watches below with my boat crew. For they'd been good to me. Not one of them ever whispered a word about the time I was so frozen with fright that I couldn't dart my iron.

We tried out and had to put in to Montevideo to ship home our oil. It looked like a good voyage for all hands. Captain Shockley wasn't wasting time on the Patagonian Grounds. He told us we were bound around Cape Horn for the Off Shore Grounds in the Pacific. He gave us all small advances on our lays, and we went ashore among the Spanish people and had a time for ourselves. Trouble was, my boat crew wouldn't let me go in some of the places I wanted to see; said I was too young. But we ate beefsteaks and drank wine and had wonderful fruits such as I never dreamed of, and Owen laid in a stock of rum—enough to last him until the end of the cruise if he was careful. Queer thing was that all hands said he was a drunkard. Well, I never saw him drunk or unable to bear his weight in boat or bark. I guess he was just uncomfortable without the stuff.

We were five days south of Montevideo when we hauled back for a gam with the ship *Charles W. Morgan*, of New Bedford. I forget her captain's name that voyage. Captain Shockley put his boat over and the mate of the *Morgan* lowered his, and we visited. *Morgan* was three years out, and we had mail for some of her crew. They were whiskered

The **CHARLES W. MORGAN**

to the eyes, ragged until you couldn't tell garment from patch, but they had had greasy luck just as we, and they were homeward bound.

The *Charles W. Morgan* was an old vessel even then, but we didn't know she was to become the most famous of all square-rigged whaleships. For she is the only one left. She was, and still is, a brave-looking ship. For eighty-five years she chased whales over all the seas of the world and brought back better than $2,000,000 for her different owners. She weathered hurricanes, cloudbursts, tornados, and typhoons. She fought off cannibals and once was almost lost when a dozen canoes tried to board her. She missed shipwreck a dozen times—once in a blind typhoon, being carried between two reefs that would have gutted her and brought to rest in the lee of a tropical island. She went on thirty-seven cruises, some of them over four years in length. She even starred in a motion picture. Yes, she played the part of Captain Ahab's ship, the *Pequod,* in the *Sea Beast,* which was the story of Moby Dick. I saw the picture nine times. There were a few things they didn't get quite right—you couldn't expect actors to harpoon and lance a whale—but it made my hair stand up just the same.

And now the *Morgan* rests quietly in a sand dock in the Mystic Historical Association whaling village in Mystic, Connecticut. It's like old times to visit there and go through the chandler shops, the sail lofts, ropewalks, smithies, and even the little church. And the *Morgan* is queen of it all. In summer, with her flags flying, she's a sight to make your heart beat quicker. And you wonder, looking at her, why she has her sides diced black and white. In those days the old-time battleships were black and white because of the gun ports. And in the danger spots where whaleships hunted their sperm, it was a good idea to let cannibals, slavers, and maybe pirates think they were battleships and armed with cannon rather than boat spades, harpoons, and muskets.

You can go aboard the *Morgan,* too. And that will give you a good idea of how whalemen lived their long years at sea. In the stern is the captain's stateroom with its little desk under the skylight so he could look up and see the compass, and his cabin with the big wide bed on gimbals and weighted underneath with rocks to keep it on an even keel in a blow. Then there are the mates' quarters, scarcely big enough for a cat to walk in, let along swing. There's the steerage, with tiny coffin bunks for the boat steerers, and for'ard, the fo'c'sle, white-limed and so tiny, you wonder how twenty-eight men could live, eat, sleep, and move around down there—with cockroaches big as mice, great ship rats, and the everlasting stink of tar, bilge, sweat, dirty clothes, and oil—without flying at each other's throats. Sometimes they did, of course. And this is how they did it. There was no fighting allowed on deck, so if a couple of foremast hands were spoiling for a battle, their shipmates took them into the fo'c'sle and made them sit on their sea chests, facing each other, within fist range. They could not stand up; their coattails were nailed to the chests to keep them seated, and a rope was stretched between them. Then they were told to go to it, but they must keep on their own side of the rope. I've seen fights where they sat and swung for minutes without touching each other while the rest of the watch below busted their sides laughing. And sometimes they fought until they couldn't sit up.

After you've been below and smelled the old oil-soaked timbers, you can climb a little way up the mizzen rigging and look down on the afterhouse, where a couple of stove boats lay. They're mashed flat, which shows you what a sperm whale can do with his jaw when he means business.

After you've seen the *Morgan,* go inside the museum. It's white, with shining brass and clean as a new pin. You'll see scrimshaw collected from all over the world. Take a good look at it. Then, someday when you're browsing in some out-of-the-way curiosity shop and you see a dusty old tooth with a faint drawing on it or a stick of bone worked into a cane, you'll know what they are. You'll buy them, I hope, take them home, clean them up, and keep them. For there is no more scrimshaw. Nowadays whales are shot with cannon, winched aboard mighty factory ships, and boiled down to make cattle fodder, fertilizer, and margarine. There's no time aboard a factory ship for scrimshaw. It's a dead art, and every piece of carved sperm tooth or pan bone is getting more and more precious. Besides being a proud memento of a grand American trade.

IX.

A FEAT OF ENDURANCE

Tilton's Walk . . . 3,000 miles over snow and ice to save the Arctic fleet.

NOT ONE OF THE thousands of visitors who boarded the *Charles W. Morgan,* until his death in 1932, ever forgot her last and most famous captain. He never took her to sea and he was retired, as the *Morgan* was when they decided to rest her solid hull in sand as a lasting memorial to the grand days of whaling. But, as the *Morgan* was the most famous ship, Captain George Fred Tilton was the most famous whale master. So what could they do but bring the two together? And that's how Captain "George Fred" was given command of the *Morgan* to welcome over 10,000 visitors aboard every year, explaining to them the workings of his ship, and spinning the splendid yarns of her adventures and his.

The courageous deed that earned him his last command is known in the dry understatement of the whaling trade as "Tilton's walk."

It happened in the terrible winter of 1897, when two

hundred castaways, crews of whaleships, were stranded on the ice 350 miles north of the Arctic Circle.

The Arctic whaling season was always a short one. The ships went through the Bering Straits in July, hunted whales twenty-fours hours a day—for the sun hardly set in summer —so they could get out before ice closed the seas in September. But winter came early that year, and many whaleships were trapped and many lives lost. Some whalemen were carried away on drifting floes, others remained aboard when most of the crews abandoned their ships and drowned when the ice shifted and let the crushed hulls sink. Some shot themselves.

The *Orca*, Captain Sherman; *Rosario*, Captain Coffin; *Jessie H. Freeman*, Captain Porter; and the *Belvedere*, Captain Millard, sailed in company for mutual protection, trying to beat the ice. But westerly gales trapped them. First *Orca*, then *Rosario* were caught and crushed by piling bergs. *Freeman*, nipped in shore ice, burned when looting shore Indians dropped a light in her oil-soaked hold. The *Belvedere*, which had picked up the crews of the other vessels, was trapped in the lee of Sea Horse Island, sixty-five miles south of Point Barrow. It was hopeless to think of getting out. All hands salvaged stores, clothing, ripped out bulkheads and timbers, and made themselves a camp. Then their captains called the uneasy men together.

"We're trapped," Captain Millard told them, "for eight months. We've stores enough for two scant meals a day, if we're careful, until next July. And if the way south isn't open by then . . ." He stopped.

"Half of us'll be dead!" someone muttered.

George Fred Tilton, third mate of the *Belvedere*, shrugged his watch coat about him. "Looks like I'll have to go fetch help," he said.

Captain Porter eyed the chunky young man with the cold pipe clenched between strong teeth.

"Ain't no help closer than the United States. You figure on walking three thousand miles, Mister?" he demanded.

"You know a better way?" Tilton replied. "Bad winter comin' up. Ain't many of us going to get through that kind of cold."

"How many men you aim to take, Mister?" Captain Millard asked.

"Don't want no one," Tilton said. "If one man can't get through, no use risking more."

They put together food enough for fifteen days, long enough to get to Point Hope, where there was a weather station, and on October 23, 1897, Tilton, with two Siberian Indians—who had shipped as guides aboard the *Orca*—pulled out with a sled, rigged with a mast and sail, and eight dogs.

Muffled in skin clothing and boots, they worked along the coast, sailing when the wind favored and carrying the dogs. The going was fair for five days, and they camped at Icy Cape.

Next morning came a southeast hurricane fit to blow the hair off a dog, as Tilton said later. The snow drove in solid masses; they couldn't see a yard ahead. The dogs, curled under the sled, howled and snapped when Tilton tried to roust them out, and the Indians refused to get out of their sleeping bags. They lay there all day with ice booming and cracking all about them and the pitiless snow blinding them.

Next day they could go on. But the Otukok River halted them again. For the hurricane had blown the ice away and left a wide stretch of open water. They followed the ice edge out to sea, Tilton ahead, testing every yard of the way, for going through the rotten shore ice would have meant death. The Indians grumbled and the dogs whined as splinters cut their pads. But by midnight they found ice ridges strong enough to get them across the river mouth.

On November 1 a northeast gale anchored them under snow for two days. Now their food was almost gone. They found more open water and detoured three miles from land before they could cross it. The ice was heaving, cracking all about them. The Indians refused to move. It was impossible to go by land, for lofty mountains came right down to the sea. In two days they covered only ten miles; every mile the sled had to be unloaded and the gear carried over twenty-foot hummocks. They ventured inshore, hauling the cowering dogs up an icy cliff. At the top another blizzard caught them, the worst they had ever seen. Impossible to put up the tent, so Tilton chopped a cave in a snowbank and the three men and eight dogs crawled into it and slept snugly for one night.

Their food was gone. They were crawling slowly through powdery snow toward Cape Lisburne when Tilton saw something ahead. The tiny specks became a party of hunting Eskimos. With brass shells, lead, and gunpowder, Tilton bought a seal from them. It was enough for one meal shared between men and dogs.

Next day they moved on. The cliff rose out of the sea to their left. But they dared not risk being carried out to sea on the offshore ice. For two days they tried to climb the cliff, hauling gear on their backs, dragging the dogs. Time after time impassable barriers halted them. Weak from hunger, they found their way back to the Eskimo hunting camp and persuaded them to sell another seal.

Now they had to risk the offshore floes. They had to carry every pound of gear, lift sled and dogs over steely ice that was slippery and treacherous. For three days they toiled, hungry, aching from countless falls. Then the ice opened before them. There was nothing but open sea. They turned, but ridge ice had piled an impassable barrier behind. The Indians looked at each other, pulled their parkas over their faces, and sat down to wait for death.

"No, ye don't!" Tilton booted them to their feet, forced snow knives into their numbed hands, and made them chop through the shelf ice until they had freed a fair-sized floe. Then he loaded sled and dogs aboard.

"Now, me lads," he told the Indians. "If this craft sinks, we'm done for. So say your prayers!"

They knelt, then climbed carefully aboard. With sail and paddles they ferried the crumbling ice floe across the open water and landed in safety. That night they slept in the angle of two ice ridges. Next day was more open water. Wearily they crossed, making their way by the gray shadow of land on their left. The dogs were failing, limping slowly, leaving bloody tracks which they licked as they moved.

They were climbing a ridge, Tilton ahead. Suddenly he signaled for quiet. Some distance off in an air hole in the ice floated several ducks. Quickly he unwrapped the shotgun from the sled, loaded it with trembling fingers, and crawled forward. Often his hands stuck to the ice, leaving strips of skin as he stalked the ducks. Then a dog barked. The ducks rose in a whirring, quacking cloud. Desperately he fired into them and saw five drop back into the hole. He raced forward and, risking frostbite, managed to retrieve one before the rest drifted under the shelf ice.

Happily he showed his prize, and they crept back toward the shore. Then one of the Indians pointed, yelling excitedly, to a great snow mound.

"A whale, by Godfrey!" Tilton shouted.

They lumbered forward, chopping into the frozen blubber. Tilton found one of the *Orca's* irons in the beast. It had been abandoned when the ice closed in. At last they had food for dogs and men. Tilton skinned his duck, boiled and ate every scrap while the Indians and dogs gulped down lumps of whalemeat until, gorged and exhausted, they crawled into the tent and slept.

During the night a strange moaning sound awakened Tilton. One side of the tent was bellying under the weight of snow and ice as a tremendous wind pressed on the tiny shelter. There was a sudden heavy gust and the tent disappeared in shreds.

"All hands." Tilton grabbed for the tattered canvas. The Indians lay still, resigned to death.

"Up." Tilton kicked madly at them. "Up. If you sleep, you'll die!"

He dragged them to their feet, raged at them until they chipped a hole in a snowbank and crawled in.

By morning the sled and dogs were buried deep and snow wreathed over them like smoke. Tilton ordered the Indians out.

"Point Hope's not far," he told them. "We'll starve if we stay here. Lash the mail to my back and we'll rope ourselves together. We'll leave the dogs and sled. Mush!"

They fought away from the camp. After a while Tilton stopped and drove his snow knife deep into the snow.

"Dirt," he said. "Too far inland. Make to starb'd."

Later, he dug again.

"Solid ice. We'm over water. Larb'd."

Wearily they tacked across the pitiless ice. Heavy squalls knocked them flat and bowled them helplessly until they fetched up against ridge ice. By night Tilton was dragging the moaning Indians through another blizzard. The ice filled his nostrils. Every breath stabbed his lungs like needles. But he fought, turning to back against the wind, breathing into his mitts to save his frozen mouth. Then he hit something solid.

"Wood," he panted.

Desperately he fumbled along a log wall. There was a muffled howl. He found a snow tunnel and crawled over a snapping husky to a door. Frantically he beat on it with numbed fists.

"Who is it?" someone called. The door opened and blessed light shone on him. "Where on earth did you come from?"

"Point Barrow," Tilton gasped. "Where am I?"

"Trading station. We're three miles from Point Hope. I'm Anderson."

The two Indians pushed into the hut and dropped, snoring, to the floor. Tilton gulped scalding coffee and munched hardtack. He puffed happily on a pipe of tobacco. Then he told Anderson of his journey.

"Let's have a look at you." Anderson dragged off his mukluks, and stared at a swollen ivory-white toe. "Frost-bite!"

Tilton almost screamed with pain as Anderson rubbed the frozen toe with snow. It was hours before circulation came back and the foot was saved from gangrene.

After resting two days he took the Indians back for the dogs. They found all but one curled under the sled. The eighth animal had been blown off a seventy-foot cliff by the blizzard.

The dead dog fed the others. Tilton got his Indians going as far as the Licbus Whaling Station at Point Hope to hand over letters from the whaling masters to Captain Nelson.

The tent was repaired and three dogs bought from local Eskimos. The two Siberians refused to go on.

So Nelson lent Tilton two Eskimos, Tickey and Canuanar, his wife.

"A good man was Tickey," Tilton said afterward, "and his wife was twice the man he was!"

On November 29 they pulled out, slowly and painfully, through rotten ice and storms of wet snow. Tilton's bad toe was blazing agony, and only the need to get help to his mates kept him moving on.

They tried the offshore ice. It was soft and pitted with open water. The dogs suffered from bleeding feet, and they had to rest three days on an ice hummock, unable to move in any direction, huddled together for warmth, their food, frozen meat and fish.

At Cape Krusenstern they found missionaries, who shared what they had to eat. Tilton bought beans, which he boiled with pork and poured onto a burlap bag to freeze. Until it was gone, he chopped off chunks as needed and heated them.

" 'Twasn't bad," he said, "when you picked out the bits of burlap—especially when you struck a paystreak of pork fat!"

They struggled on, fearful always that their food would give out. Blizzards held them for days. Then, the little sail set, they made as much as twenty miles in a day.

By Christmas they were at Buckland River. They left the coast there to cut across the Seward Peninsula.

The Eskimos knew no trail over land. Their food ran out; Tilton killed the two weakest dogs to feed the rest, and the humans ate the last of the frozen fish. But they dared not rest.

By January 1, 1898, they reached Unalakleet and rested at the Swedish Mission. Next day Tilton was moving on when two men called him back to the mission.

"A revenue cutter is on the way to help your mates," he was told.

He learned that some whaleships that had escaped the ice had reported those trapped. So the U.S. Government had sent Lieutenant Jarvis of the cutter *Bear* as far as the ice would let her go and Jarvis and Dr. Call were on their way to Teller near Nome to drive a herd of reindeer to Point Lay, where they could be slaughtered to feed the whalemen. But the deer had to feed themselves, which was almost impossible in the deep snow, as they went north.

"Not much chance of getting the whole herd through," they had told the missionary.

"I'll be getting on then," Tilton said.

Two days later he reached an Army post at St. Michaels, Tickey and Canuanar stumping bravely behind him. The soldiers were astonished at his thousand-mile journey, and gave him food and fresh clothing. He took off with three sleds, one laden with Army mail, since no ship could get out to the United States. Tilton planned to go up the Yukon River to Dawson and through Seventy Mile Pass to Valdez. But the river was frozen solid, and a steamer, caught in the ice, reported famine and food riots in Dawson. Tilton could have made a fortune then and there by packing food to the gold capital, but he didn't. He made it as far as Andreafski, and had to stay there to rest his frostbitten foot.

Now came the hardest part of his fabulous journey. It was 57 below zero, and the snow, deep and powdery. For five days he searched the Kiskokwim Mountains for a pass and found none. The dogs were snow-blind and exhausted under the whips of the Eskimos. But the party kept going, killing the weakest dogs to feed the rest. Finally, after days of struggling over jagged rocks and deep drifts, they managed to cross the western slopes of the mountains and saw flat lake country ahead.

Tilton was thin as a rail, his eyes bloodshot with glare,

his foot in agony day and night. They reached a lake. He set sails on two sleds and, towing the third, sailed for a whole day to cross it.

By the time they reached the coast again, six dogs were gone from the twenty-four they took from St. Michaels. Tilton gave one sled to local Indians and bought food for themselves and the teams. Ten days later they camped at Nushsgok on the way to Katmai, where the Alaska Commercial Company had a station and, they hoped, a ship to take them to the United States. They fought blizzards every inch of the way, the dogs struggling to keep trail, the Eskimos, even the wonderful Canuanar, weeping hopelessly. And it was three long horrible weeks before they found only a miserable cluster of Indians huts and the heartbreaking news that the Alaska Commercial Company was over on Kodiak Island.

Tilton stared across the Shelikof Straits—thirty-seven miles of sea so treacherous that big ships avoided it whenever possible. And there was no way across. He searched village and beach and finally found a derelict dory so damaged it "wouldn't hold punkins." But he wasn't a whaleman for nothing. He gave the dogs to local Indians, dismantled the sleds, and using the sinew lashings, *sewed* that old dory together, calking the gaping seams with what was left of his woolen long johns and a skin parka.

He loaded the dory with mail and gear, placing Tickey and Canuanar in the stern with bailers. The sky was gray and the sea rough with floating ice. Water leaked through the sides as soon as he pulled from shore.

"Bail," he commanded.

He pulled in a short whaleman's stroke until his back was a dull agony, his frostbitten foot torment, and his hands raw. But he dared not stop. The Eskimos bailed madly as the shore receded and they tossed in bleak, icy waters. Darkness overtook them, and Tilton, mumbling in delirium, kept rowing. He was singing to himself when the keel hit gravel. They crawled ashore, dragged the boat clear, and dropped, unconscious, beside it. That night a howling tempest whipped the strait to lashing foam.

"We'd never have lived a minute in that," Tilton said grimly.

Now they searched the island, working around the coast, beaching the leaky boat in every cove to bail her out. It was dark before the barking of dogs told them they had reached at last the Alaska Company at St. Paul.

Herron, the agent, looked them over silently, didn't reply to Tilton's greeting, and reached for the letters he had brought. After he had read them, he looked at the man who had walked all across Alaska to save his mates.

"You can have food and a place to sleep if you've got the price," he said.

"Well." Tilton eyed the mean little man. "Looks like I'm back in civilization again. I'll not trouble you long, Mister. All I want is passage to somewhere where I can ship to the States so I can get food back to my shipmates."

"Prince William's two hundred miles from here," Herron mumbled. "I got a schooner, the *Saint Paul;* you can take passage in her. Seven thousand dollars!"

"You cussed bloodsucker," Tilton raged. "Everywhere I touched, people have been good; shared what food they had and gave me all the help they could. And no mention of pay. I got a good mind to tie a knot in your neck. Seven thousand dollars for a two-hundred-mile passage!"

"Take it or leave it." Herron grinned.

Tilton signed a contract on behalf of the *Belvedere* for food, clothing, and the schooner passage. Four days later the dirty little vessel put out and ran into a northeast gale that kept them hove to for two days. Then the captain declared himself lost. Captain George Fred took command, made a sextant observation, and sailed the schooner into Port Etches; then he transshipped himself and his two Eskimos to the gasoline schooner *Albion.*

In five days he was at Portland with fifty cents in his pocket. He gave that to an expressman to carry the Army mail to the post office. And there he was, broke, two Eskimos dependent on him, and not even his *Albion* passage paid for.

So he borrowed enough to send a wire to his owners in New Bedford, explaining his plight and asking for $500 to get him to San Francisco, where he could get stores. His owner said if he was in Portland, he must have deserted his ship, and wouldn't send him a cent.

He went back to the *Albion,* borrowed enough to wire for his life savings, $450. They let him and his Eskimos stay aboard the schooner until the money came. Then he paid his debt and had enough to book passage to San Francisco where, he hoped, the agents for the trapped ships would give him food to take back to them.

By the time he arrived, he was famous. Army dispatches and telegrams from the stations through which he had passed had sent reports of his gallant march, and newspapers printed many interviews with him.

The agents of the *Belvedere* wired the owner in New Bedford, stating that it was indeed Tilton who had asked them for money and that he had marched the whole way from the Arctic Circle. After some delay the owners replied authorizing the agents to pay Tilton $100 on his personal I.O.U! He used that money to buy passage for Tickey and Canuanar back to Point Hope. They were glad to be away from the noisy, frightening white man's city, and left happily, clothed in such magnificence as they had never dreamed of, and laden with presents that would make them rich forever.

Later the owner wrote, asking Tilton to go north and rejoin his ship.

"He didn't say how I was to get there," Captain George Fred said later. "So I wrote and asked him if he expected me to walk back!"

But from one point of view, that heartbreaking journey was in vain. For the same day that Tilton arrived in San Francisco, April 17, 1898, what was left of the reindeer herd arrived in Point Lay. The revenue cutter *Bear* reached the stranded whalemen July 22 with a doctor and medicines to treat the sick and scurvy-ridden. And by the end of that month those whaleships able to sail were free of the ice and headed south.

And Captain George Fred's famous "walk" was done.

In the Seamen's Bethel in New Bedford, that chapel made famous by Herman Melville's description of Preacher Mapple's sermon to the crew of the Pequod *before they embarked on their terrible search for Moby Dick, is a bronze plaque subscribed by hundreds of whaling families.*

IN MEMORY OF
CAPTAIN
GEORGE FRED TILTON
1861 ~ 1932
WHALEMAN
WHO
IN 1897 WALKED 3000 MILES
THROUGH ALASKAN WINTER TO
SAVE THE LIVES OF 200 MEN
ON FOUR WHALESHIPS CAUGHT
IN ARCTIC ICE.

X.

WE ROUND CAPE HORN

Death of Stan Dunbar . . . Battle between a sperm whale and a giant squid . . . The Globe *Mutiny.*

WE WERE BOUND around the Horn! After passing between the Falklands and the Patagonia Coast, we sighted the island of Los Estados, where we took our final bearing for the long tangents around the dreaded cape. We took down the fore and main topgallant masts and changed all sail for heavy weather canvas. All hands were set to making chafing gear, for straps and lines rubbed thin might mean the death of our ship.

Two days southeast of the island the sky grew dark, an ugly chill wind came out of the west, and what had been long, sleepy swells changed to gray-black cliffs of water, edged and marbled with spume. They charged at us like armies and slammed our hull until she shuddered; icy water squirted through seams into the fo'c'sle until they packed the for'ard bunks with old clothes and dunnage to keep it out.

It was misery; not a dry spot in the ship. It was all hands every hour of the day and night, clinging to rigging with the wind tearing the reefers off us, foot ropes icy and treacherous, our hands too numb to grip and our teeth chattering with cold. For four days we had nothing warm but coffee. There was no afterguard and fo'c'sle now, all hands jumped to the Captain's orders as the reeling vessel plunged and pitched through seas that lifted main yard high and thundered on our deck like the hammers of doom.

On the fifth day the wind veered to the N.N.E., and before noon we were plunged into the thickest, coldest fog I ever saw. The heavy seas still hit us with great booming crashes and the rail and spars were dusted with ice. Everything was wet: blankets, spare clothing, even our bunks. But there was still some beef left from Montevideo and we had hot meals again.

I heard that Nelson, the townie, was making trouble. He'd grown into something like a man, what with hard work and the plain food of the *Canton*. But as he found his strength, he used it on his mates. He had a scruff of pink whiskers by now, talked big, wearing his scrimshaw knucks in the safety of the fo'c'sle and swearing he'd do for Mr. Coffin, the Third Mate. Coffin had taken his boot to Nelson when he came aboard, falling down drunk at Montevideo; said he was a disgrace to the ship. Nelson hadn't forgotten it.

"He's got a nasty look in his eye," Jimmy Leeds told me. "Shouldn't wonder if he gets himself in a bind before long."

But we had no time to worry about Nelson. After three days of dense fog, all hands were jumpy as cats. We still rolled heavily, though the seas were calmer. The decks were wet and water dripped from the rigging. We couldn't see more than a man length and the masts disappeared before they were ten feet above the deck. Men, moving along the lifelines, appeared like ghosts, starting back from each other when they met and hailing nervously like strangers meeting in a perilous place for the first time. It was as though every man was alone in a prison of blinding cloud. Only the binnacle showed a faint green glow, and the helmsman's face bent over it like a death's head, scanning carefully, for there was a powerful drift to the northwest, toward the dreaded Horn itself. We sailed by dead reckoning, searching for a westing that would carry us safely past the Horn. And the watches below whispered of derelicts haunting the icy waters, of homeward bound whaleships and collisions in the fog. No one slept on watch in those waters.

Then just as night was changing the space around us from gray to black, a booming came out of the north, a vicious lash of rain and the fog was ripped away like dirty muslin. And all about us the mountainous seas, green-black and littered with ice, came smashing over the bow, breaking on the tryworks and foaming down about the helmsman's feet.

"All hands!" the Mate shouted.

We jumped to shorten sail, the wind rattling our oilskins while we fought to hold fast. The wind veered until it was dead astern and the *Canton* was shoved forward like a kitten by a broom, each sea burying us until the deck was knee deep. Captain Shockley snatched the wheel and put us off a few points to save the following seas from pooping us. We jumped to secure the boats and double-lash the spares. All night we stood to, our ears deafened by the crash of waves and the frantic howl of the wind, our hats tied on with kerchiefs under our chins, oilskins belted with spun yarn, our slimy leather seaboots slipping and sliding every which way. By midnight all was secure, but there was no watch below. The cook passed out coffee. It was all he could manage with his galley soaring like a carnival swing, and we wedged ourselves in whatever lee we could find to sip and gasp over the scalding brew.

For three days and three nights the *Canton* labored, creaking like an overloaded basket as the seas pounded and shook her. Captain Shockley stood by the wheel like a statue for every minute of that time. It was worse by day. We could see the sky filled with torn and racing clouds and the mountainous, blustering seas battering us like nightmares conjured up by a devil to destroy us. We had shipped a rail of one-inch round iron across the space where the cutting-in stage was made fast. It had no resistance to the water, but a sea mounted us and twisted that iron two ways like a boy might twist chewing gum. And later I saw a port, eight inches across and three thick, that was starred—not knocked out of its frame, but starred—as though it had been hit by a sledge hammer. And when I looked at the water that could do that, I felt afraid right down to my bones.

The gale grew worse. The *Canton* pitched until mountainous breakers buried her to the foremast. Then she rose heavily, like an old woman getting up from her knees, and tons of water she had shoveled up roared along the deck to break against masts and houses. Then one morning we made out a thin line of yellow along the eastern horizon. There was sun somewhere, and that gave us a little comfort. But in the afternoon came sleet that cut our faces and froze on our reefers and made the deck a rink. Both pumps were manned, and the water came out clear; it meant we were leaking badly.

But Cape Horn wasn't finished with us. I slipped once and would have gone overboard if it hadn't been for Mr. Coffin, who snatched my collar and nearly broke my neck hauling me to safety. For the sea was playing with us like a young dog worrying a rag toy. We shook and plunged and skidded, and the pumps were kept going day and night. It was at night that the bowsprit carried away. The *Canton* fetched up into the wind and lay over until I thought she'd capsize. We lay until daylight, the boom slamming the bow until no one dared go into the fo'c'sle. We went overside in monkey ropes to cut away the riffle. I was one, clinging to the striker stay and chopping every time the wreckage came clear of the icy water. Jimmy Leeds was close by, his thin face blue with cold, and Big Olaf, shoulder deep and, so help me, whistling, as he wrestled the splintered boom. The bow came up as the wreckage drifted clear, and we climbed aboard, soaked to the skin and so cold we couldn't speak. We stumbled aft along the lifelines like bugs and changed into clothing that was only a little less wet than that which we took off. Then there was coffee. And I didn't refuse a tot of Montevideo brandy Owen dragged from under his reefer.

Then it was snow until our deck was a foot deep, and ice floating on our larboard beam. Captain Shockley risked changing course to the northwest. We were rounding the Cape, the Mate said, but who could see it?

Then, in the afternoon it was, the snow had stopped and there was a chill yellowish light on the tossing sea.

"Blo-o-o-ws!" someone yelled. "Blo-o-o-ws!"

"Where away?" Captain Shockley called.

"Larb'd beam. Sperm! There he breaches!"

"Surely he ain't going to lower in this!" Owen gasped.

He didn't. But we watched something I never saw again in all my years of whaling. Not a cable length off a sperm whale shot out of the water half his length and crashed back again, thrashing his flukes in the yeasty sea. He rolled, jaw out, and we made out something horrible clinging to his head. Once a tremendous wave lifted him and we saw, like through a green window, his whole length. Again and again he breached, shaking his mighty head and trying to open his jaws. But he couldn't. For twined about his head was a giant squid, its ten arms wound like cables about him. I was mesmerized. I saw the staring eyes of that monster, and they were big as deadlights in the flabby green body. Once two of the legs waved and clamped down again as the whale rolled. Owen said they must have been upward of forty feet long. We passed them with the whale thrashing and breaching in the terrible seas, and they were far astern when the battle ceased.

"You've seen a sperm killed," Leeds told me. "That bull is dead, sure as shooting, and the horror that killed him is the only living thing besides man that could do it."

"Like a sea serpent." Pete Brava shivered.

It was that same day that a shaft of sunlight came through the dirt-colored clouds and showed us a jagged gray mass to the northeast.

"Take a good look." It was Captain Shockley standing beside me. "That's Cape Horn!"

I took my look and knew I'd always recognize that enemy of wind-ship sailors.

But we were happier now we'd seen Cape Stiff and knew we were past. We had rigged a jury staysail to the knightheads and were tacking in a northwesterly direction until fog closed us in again. We hove to, for the land was too close abeam. When the fog cleared, we saw land again, and that day Stan Dunbar of the Second Mate's watch fell off the main yard, hit the edge of the midship house, and broke his neck. The Mate picked him up and took him to his own cabin to wait for calmer weather before burying him. It was four days before we hove to off Desolation Island at the western end of the Straits of Magellan. And we had been pumping all the way.

We mustered, hats off and shivering in the cold, the foremast hands for'ard, the boat steerers and afterguard aft of the long plank on which lay Stan Dunbar, sewn into a piece of canvas weighted with good Massachusetts rock and covered with the flag. Captain Shockley read the service, and Mr. Nanton tilted the plank. Stan slid into the sea and disappeared. We stood around, staring into the gray water, thinking it might easily be one of us next time.

"All hands," Mr. Nanton bawled. He wasn't giving us time to mope. "All hands to rig the bowsprit."

It took us two days to ship the new boom and make all secure. Then came the changing of foul weather sails and the replacing of the upper masts. We found a rotted piece in a bilge plank, patched and calked it, rigged a canvas and tar patch strong enough to hold for the rest of the cruise, and pumped our ship dry, or as dry as a whaleship can be pumped. Then we got under way for the Off Shore Grounds.

It was the second day after lookouts were posted that Nelson ran athwart Mr. Coffin again. Nelson had been shirking ever since we passed Los Estados, and when the Third Mate gave him an order, he let go with some lip. So Mr. Coffin backed him against the rail and told him what he'd do if Nelson didn't quit jawing back. Nelson tried to knock his hand away and clouted Coffin across the jaw. Maybe it was an accident, but aboard a whaleship it's mutiny to strike an officer no matter how it happens. But Coffin didn't call for irons; he just stepped back and let Nelson have one punch in the jaw. Nelson went down and stayed there.

"Now," Coffin said. "You keep to leeward of me from now

on. You'll jump when I say so or I'll have you in irons for the rest of the cruise. Savvy?"

Nelson got up and went below without another word.

I began to hear things as we moved north; Nelson had threatened to do for the Third Mate. I took little notice until one evening I'd come down from masthead and was passing under the midship house on my way aft for some coffee. Mr. Coffin was going for'ard, and just as he went under the house, a spare guy block from the cutting tackle hit the deck with a crash, not a foot from the Third Mate's foot. Then I saw Nelson drop from the house, dodge around the tryworks, and duck below just as Coffin ran aft to see who was on the house. I hurried to my quarters; a boat steerer is neither officer nor foremast hand. I had to stay neutral, even if Mr. Coffin had saved my life. But I decided to keep an eye on Nelson and maybe square things with Coffin.

The Third Mate caught Nelson again. He was lounging in the bow and showing another hand his scrimshaw knucks and boasting what he'd do with them.

"I'll take those," Coffin said, coming around the tryworks.

Nelson said nothing, but his little eyes were mean as a mink's.

"You've no right to carry a weapon," Coffin said quietly. "Hand it over, or do I have to take it from you?"

Nelson stood there and started to shake. His face was yellow with temper, but he didn't say anything. Coffin took the knuckles from him and threw them overboard.

"Now get below, you punk!" he said scornfully.

For a second I thought Nelson would jump him. He glared at the Third Mate like a cornered rat. Then he went to the fo'c'sle scuttle and disappeared.

On my watch below I went for'ard to talk to Owen and found the fo'c'sle in an uproar. Owen, his beard matted with blood, was sitting on his sea chest, looking shaky. Nelson, drunk as a lord, was storming up and down the narrow space, screaming that he'd do for Coffin and the whole afterguard. The rest of the watch below looked on silently.

"What you after down here?" Nelson yapped as soon as he saw me. "Spyin' for the afterguard? Boat steerers ain't wanted in the fo'c'sle."

"He's welcome here," Owen mumbled through cut and swollen lips.

"You want some more, Pop?" Nelson sneered. "You want some more teeth knocked out?"

"You scummy thief," Owen spat. "Stole my liquor, he did. Now he's drunk-brave and talking mutiny. Mutiny! That bilge rat!"

Nelson jumped for him. I stepped between them and the thief halted. Then he whirled, dashed to his bunk, snatched up a link of chain, and clenched it in his fist. He was at me before I could guard properly. His weighted fist caught me on the side of the head and knocked me flat. I squirmed away from his stamping feet and got up. He came at me, raving. I ducked his wild swing and jabbed him in the stomach; then, when he bent over, I hit him in the jaw. He staggered back, spitting filthy talk, and grabbed a bottle from his bunk. Owen put his foot out as Nelson charged. He went down and came up like a cat. I hit him twice before he could use his bottle, grabbed him, and threw him into his bunk. The others didn't say anything, though they might have resented a boat steerer fighting in the only place aboard that was theirs. But I guess that most of them had felt the weight of Nelson's fists.

"Very good," Owen said. "Very good indeed, young fellow.

Now, just pass me back what's left of the bottle that pig stole. And watch out; he may have a knife in that rat's nest!"

I gave it to him and he took a careful swig, wincing as the rough spirits stung his broken lips. Then he looked over to where Nelson glared groggily from his bunk.

"So you're the brave bucko who's going to take the ship? You cheap, back-alley tough; you ain't man enough to lead mice, let alone men. You think any of us would follow you against our afterguard? And don't think you'll get the jump on me again; I'm not turning my back on the likes of you no more." He carefully stowed away his bottle, fished out his pipe, and lit it.

"Mutineers!" he scoffed. "You ever hear of a hand named Comstock? He was a back-alley punk, just like you, Nelson; thought he was a mutineer, too. Listen to what happened to him and see if you still want to take the ship."

Samuel Comstock was all and more than Jimmy Owen called him. He had made three whaling cruises and was already known as a sea lawyer and troublemaker when he signed as boat steerer aboard the *Globe* of Nantucket, Captain Thomas Worth.

The *Globe* sailed in December, 1822, and from the start young Comstock—he was nineteen—was a problem. He was a good-looking husky fellow with a swagger like a bull terrier and a temper to match. The crew soon saw that he took no back talk from anyone, afterguard or fo'c'sle. He spent a lot of time for'ard; he wasn't too proud to mix with the foremast hands, and they thought he was one fine fellow. The afterguard thought differently. Food was poor, like on all whaleships, but it was Comstock, instead of one of the fo'c'sle hands, who headed the complaints to the Captain.

"He's getting too big for his britches," Captain Worth decided.

It was over a year from port that Comstock got his come-uppance. The ship had hauled back for a gam with another vessel and there were visitors aboard the *Globe*. Comstock had to play big before them, too. So he challenged Nathaniel Fisher, third mate of the *Globe,* to a friendly wrestling match.

Fisher had had plenty of lip from Comstock, and he figured Comstock wanted to show him up before the crew and visitors. Anyway Fisher was tougher than the boat steerer thought. He threw Comstock easily. And when he did it the second time, Comstock got up and let go with his fists. Fisher could have put him in irons, but he didn't. He knocked Comstock down again. The boat steerer, mad with rage that he was looking a fool before his mates, sprang to his feet, cursing, and rushed the Third Mate. Fisher waited, and knocked him kicking. Comstock got up slowly, aware of the grins of the onlookers, and eyed Fisher.

"All right, Mister," he whispered. "I'll get you. Don't ever forget that. I'll fix you!"

But he didn't do anything—then. He hated Fisher for making him look small before the foremast hands. He hated him worse because his own authority suffered; men don't like a leader that they have seen licked. But he went among them whispering about what he intended to do when the time came.

The *Globe* put in at Oahu in the Sandwich Islands, and six hands, tired of hardtack, jumped ship. Captain Worth took on six more; the sorriest scrapings in the Pacific, drunken beachcombers he wouldn't have looked at if he hadn't been shorthanded. But they were right for Comstock; just the help he needed to get his own back on Fisher, and all the rest of them, too! He got the new hands in corners and sounded them out on a plan to seize the ship, loot her, and land on some remote little island where they could live like kings for the rest of their lives.

It sounded fine, but it needed one more touch of pepper to make it cook right. One of the new hands got saucy with the Captain one morning and was flogged. That did the trick. They were ripe for anything that would give them revenge, especially a rich ship, weapons, and the chance of a safe and idle future.

Carefully they made their plans, and not one of the rest of the crew dared mention a word, they were so scared of the desperadoes.

One midnight Comstock padded aft. The helmsman eyed the knife in his hand and trembled. Grinning, Comstock lit a lantern and crept below to the large cabin. As he reached it, three other mutineers stole in from the steerage alleyway. Two posted themselves at the First Mate's cabin door and the room shared by Second Mate John Lumbard and Nat Fisher. Comstock put the lantern on the table, took a razor-sharp ax from the third man, and crept into the Captain's stateroom.

It was a sweltering night, and the Captain was sleeping in a hammock slung across his stateroom. Comstock licked his lips, took a look around, measured his distance, and chopped twice. Lantern light from the table outside flickered on a headless corpse.

Blood from head to waist, Comstock saw that Payne, the man he had chosen for partner, had opened the Mate's door, and as he watched, stabbed at the sleeping man with a boarding knife. But the Mate wasn't killed. He floundered out of his bunk, saw them, and called their names loud enough for the other mates to hear.

"Help!" he cried.

"Too late." Comstock grinned.

The wounded mate rushed him. They went down on the blood-smeared deck, Payne dancing about, afraid to strike with his murderous boarding knife for fear of killing Comstock. But Comstock tore free, seized the ax and, as the Mate struggled to rise, brained him.

The lantern had gone out, but it was sure the Second and Third mates were awake. Leaving Payne and the two others to guard them, Comstock lit the lantern and ran into the Captain's room. There were two muskets in the rack. He loaded both and mounted a bayonet on one. He crept back, motioned the others aside and, aiming in the direction he thought the mates might lie, he fired through the door. As the powder choked them they heard a whimper of pain.

"I'm shot!" It was Fisher. "I'm shot in the mouth!"

"Open up!" Comstock ordered.

He heard movement and handed the lantern to Payne. Then he held the bayonet musket ready. The door opened. Comstock lunged at the dark figure behind it. The man ducked back and Comstock tripped over the high door sill. Lumbard jumped him before the other mutineers could get in, and when he got to his feet, Fisher, blood dripping from his shattered jaw, was holding the bayonet to his chest.

For a moment Fisher's finger tightened on the trigger. He glared at the bloodstained wretch before him and felt himself fainting with pain and loss of blood.

"Look, Mister," Comstock said gently. "It's all over. We've took the ship, Captain and Mate are dead, and the whole crew are behind me. You haven't got a chance, Mister. Now, you just pass that musket to me and I'll save your life. I'll tell them you've surrendered. They'll put you ashore safe, Mister. Come on, let's have it."

Fisher, his wits dulled by his wound, handed over the

musket. With a yell of triumph Comstock snatched the weapon, shoved Fisher back and, as Lumbard tried to reach it, pinned the Second Mate to the bulkhead. Comstock jerked the weapon free and Lumbard dropped.

"Now, cully"—he grinned at Fisher—"it's your turn. Remember, I told you you'd pay for besting me. You've had your last wrestle, Mister. You're going to die!"

"After you promised me my life," Fisher mumbled. "I could have killed you but I believed you'd keep your word. What a fool I was. Anyway, I'll die like a man, which is more than you'll do when your time comes—and soon!'

He turned his back. Comstock aimed. The bayonet was touching the back of the Third Mate's head when he fired.

Then Comstock went berserk. Again and again he stabbed the bayonet into Lumbard's body, then he raced on deck, blood from head to foot, and ran up and down glaring at the shocked crew and waving the bayoneted musket.

"Fetch the Captain up here!" he howled.

The headless body was brought and heaved overboard. The Mate's corpse was passed up and thrown overside. Then Second Mate Lumbard was dragged over the smeared deck. He lay, blood leaking from dozens of wounds. But he moved.

"He's alive," someone muttered.

"Over with him!"

But Lumbard managed somehow to cling to the bulwark, begging piteously for mercy, until Comstock stamped on his fingers. Fisher's body went last. Then they heard splashing and faint cries. Lumbard was *still alive,* feebly swimming after the ship. But not for long. Sharks, attracted by the blood, saw to that.

Now Comstock was the big man he had pretended to be. He appointed Payne mate and took over the Captain's cabin for himself. But he trusted no one. He gave different courses every few hours to baffle the crew, and eventually sighted one of the Marshall Islands. He put a boat over for provisions, and when the natives came off, he shot one for some trifling offense and sailed away. At another island the natives were friendly and joined an orgy of drinking and other excesses on board the *Globe*.

Then one of the crew was found to possess a pistol. That man was promptly hanged. Comstock now became suspicious of everyone. He locked up all arms and made the crew move in to the after part of the ship, where their talk could be overheard. He read new articles to them. Anyone failing to report a sail would be put to death. Anyone refusing to fight would die by being boiled in oil in the tryworks!

On sailed the death ship, the crew sullen now and afraid of the two murderers who commanded them. Then, only two weeks after the mutiny, land was sighted again. It was Mili Atoll, one of the Marshall group, a ring of coral containing many little islands. It was off the usual lane of ships, and the *Globe* dropped anchor just inside the entrance to the reef. Canoes came out with fresh food, water, and fruit, the islanders delighted that the great ship had come to visit them.

It was here that Comstock began to double-cross his fellow mutineers.

For some time Silas Payne had been hard to handle; he'd taken as many chances as Comstock; why should the boat steerer be the lord high muck-a-muck? Comstock went back to his old tactics. The plan was to unload the ship and make camp ashore. Later, perhaps, they could burn the old *Globe*. Rafts were built and the crew set to ferrying supplies to the beach. Comstock had a canvas shelter made for himself and left Payne aboard the *Globe* in charge of unloading.

The friendly natives came crowding down the beach and stood around coveting all the fine knives and axes and clothing the *papalangis* had. And Comstock, unusual for him, became very generous. Payne, watching suspiciously through a glass from the ship, saw Comstock handing over hardtack, clothing, trinkets, until the islanders were skipping about and almost worshiping the kind white captain. So that was it. Payne figured that Comstock, suspicious of the crew, was seeing to it that he had plenty of followers among the natives in case he wanted to turn them against his shipmates. Promptly Payne sent word for Comstock to stop giving away the ship's supplies—or else! Comstock ordered Payne ashore. Payne tucked a revolver in his belt, took the next boat to the beach, and shoved into Comstock's tent. The mutineers, many of them thoroughly terrified of the murderers, tried to hear what was going on between their leaders. There was a lot of angry mumbling, then Comstock came out and ordered a boat to the *Globe*. After a while he returned with a cutlass slung from his belt. He said nothing; just walked up the beach in the direction of the native town.

"He's gone," Payne said, "and good riddance. But keep a sharp lookout; he might come back looking for trouble."

It was almost dark when a lookout gave the alarm. Coming down the beach was a great crowd of natives, with Comstock in the lead.

"Stand by!" Payne shouted.

But the islanders weren't armed. They just marched to the camp, looked it over, and returned up the beach.

"He's got something up his sleeve," Payne said uneasily. "Coming back at night to murder us all, like as not."

"Wonder how many muskets he's given them?" a hand muttered.

Payne sent men aboard the *Globe* for all the weapons available. Then they set up breastworks in the sand, passed out boarding knives, harpoons, cutting-in spades, and lances. To four of the beachcombers who had come aboard at Oahu, Payne gave muskets and took one himself.

"Watch and watch," he ordered. "Shoot anything you see moving!"

At times during the long night they heard drums and the hoot of conches from the village, but the beach was deserted.

Just at dawn a sentry shouted. Payne rushed out of the tent, musket in hand. Far up the beach they saw Comstock sneaking along in the shadow of some trees.

"Watch him," Payne whispered. "Fire when I do!"

They waited a long time. There was movement in the cover near camp. Comstock peered over a thicket. Then he stepped into the open. He was drawing his cutlass when he saw the five muskets aimed at him.

"Don't shoot!" he screamed. "I won't hurt you!"

The muskets banged. As the smoke cleared they saw Comstock face down in the sand. Payne snatched up an ax, ran over, and with one blow almost severed Comstock's head.

"Bury him," he panted.

They scraped a hole in the sand, wrapped Comstock and his cutlass in a strip of canvas and shoveled sand on him.

"Now I'm the captain," Payne bawled.

Though that was the end of Comstock, it was not the end of the *Globe* mutiny. Payne sent six men to man the *Globe*, still riding at anchor, and set the rest to strengthen camp against a surprise attack.

But the six men aboard had had enough of mutiny and murder. That night while the shore party slept, they slipped the cable, drifted out of the lagoon, and by dawn were gone.

Payne and his four gunmen were now in charge. There were two whaleboats left on the beach. One was dismantled to strengthen the other enough to carry them to another island in case the natives attacked.

But they didn't, yet. They came back with fruit and coconuts. Whalemen went to their village, took what they wanted, and terrorized the islanders with their muskets. Payne kidnaped a girl, flogged her, and put her in irons when she tried to run away from him. The islanders watched silently.

But there were two young men who did not join in the general looting of the native town. Cyrus Hussey of Nantucket and William Lay of Saybrook, Connecticut, made friends with a chief and an elderly couple. They reported to Payne that the islanders resented the cruel treatment they were receiving. Payne decided to show them who was boss. On the pretext that a hatchet had been stolen, Payne and his four gunmen seized a hostage, bound him, and took him with them to the village. They found a hatchet, but no one would confess to its theft. The islanders crowded close, silent but threatening. The mutineers decided to retreat. The islanders followed.

"About face," someone muttered.

The four turned and faced the natives, muskets ready. Some carried small bags, they noticed. Then they saw those in the rear take round stones from the bags, place them in slings, and a stone hit one of the mutineers in the forehead. They fired but the natives didn't run. More stones whizzed over. The whalemen broke and ran. With chilling yells the islanders chased them. Slings whirred and stones hit with deadly accuracy. A whaleman went down, his head cracked. The others made it to camp.

The islanders raced off, returning with spears and swords made of shark teeth bound to wooden blades. Payne gathered his men about the built-up whaleboat. Then he called for a parley. A chief came forward.

He had agreed, Payne told the whalemen, to hand over everything to the islanders and to obey their laws; in return their lives would be spared.

The islanders rushed to loot the camp. But the couple who had befriended William Lay grabbed him and dragged him off. He was about to try and escape when he saw the natives were attacking. He watched two whalemen running, but they were cut down and their skulls smashed. An old man speared Payne and another native ran to stab Lay, but his friends threw him down and shielded him with their bodies. Then they dragged him into cover and kept him there until all the whalemen were dead.

It was the next day that he saw a group of natives with Cyrus Hussey.

"What are they going to do with us?" Lay whispered.

"Nothing. They're friends, I think."

They were separated, Lay remaining with his friends, Hussey with the chief of a nearby island, and they lived for a year and a half among the islanders of Mili Atoll. They learned the language, joined the feasts and dances, and people came from distant islands to see the strange white men.

In June, 1824, a whaleship tacked into Valparaiso harbor. There were only six men aboard and they, half starved; the ship was filthy, without gear or boats, and her sails were rotted. She had sailed across the Pacific with no navigator and no aid but a compass. She was the *Globe*.

The six men reported the mutiny, and Michael Hogan, U.S. consul at Valparaiso, had to arrest them. A new captain was appointed to the *Globe* and the six men went home to stand trial. But the ringleaders had to be found, and the U.S. schooner *Dolphin,* Lt. Commander John Percival, sailed for Mili Atoll.

The natives were friendly, but they knew nothing of white whalemen. Nevertheless there were spars, boat gear and craft with the *Globe* mark. Lieutenant Paulding, U.S.N., searched the islands for survivors, but as soon as he was sighted, Lay and Hussey were spirited away, until Paulding spotted a small, furtive canoe and gave chase. The canoe beached and its three occupants ran for cover. Paulding put over a boat and started for the beach. But he saw the islanders gathered and their women running into the bush. That meant they were ready to fight. Then a tall man ran down the shore.

"They're going to kill you," he shouted. "Don't come ashore."

"Who are you?" Paulding shouted.

"William Lay, of the *Globe.*"

"Run to the water. I'll pick you up!"

"I'd never make it; they've got slings!"

Paulding ordered his men to shore. As the boat touched, he ran for Lay, put a pistol to his head.

"Tell them I'll shoot the first man to attack!"

The old man who had befriended Lay came forward slowly, weeping. Lay explained what he must do, and the old man went back.

"How many more alive?" Paulding demanded.

"Only one, Hussey." Lay pointed to the island where his mate lived.

The boat put off. Paulding held a pistol on the chief until Hussey surrendered.

"Do you wish to go home?" Paulding asked.

"Yes, sir," Hussey said. "I know of nothing I have done for which I'd be afraid to go home!"

The *Dolphin* sailed with the two survivors of the bloodiest mutiny in the history of American whaling. Comstock's skeleton was uncovered and the true story of the mutiny published. It was found that the survivors were forced by their terror of the ringleader and they were pardoned.

The *Globe* sailed on one more whaling voyage. But she was a doomed ship, a haunted vessel. She was sold out in 1828, taken to Buenos Aires, and broken up.

XI.

CANNIBAL WHALES

Honolulu . . . A deserter . . . My adventure with a lumpy horse . . . Fighting a whale with a sheath knife.

WE HAD NO MORE mutinous talk from Master Nelson, though he sulked for days and spat every time he passed astern of Mr. Coffin. We heard from the cook that Captain Shockley intended to work the Offshore Grounds, discovered by the *Globe* in 1818 on the voyage previous to the mutiny —a feeding area for sperm lying between the latitudes 3 and 10 south, and longitudes 90 to 120 degrees west. After that we would fish along the Line and transship our oil at Honolulu.

Even though we were passaging, the lookouts were manned during the daylight hours. But they sighted nothing but porpoises. Our fresh food was soon done. The nanny goat refused to provide milk for the Captain's coffee, so we ate her and her mate, who had been making himself a nuisance by butting everyone who went near his favorite spot, a patch of shade under the carpenter's bench. Even the water was getting ropy before we sighted a small cluster of islands.

"Just the landfall for you, Nelson," Jimmy Owen called when we dropped anchor off a rocky shore. "That's Robinson Crusoe Island!"

It was Juan Fernández, belonging to Chile. A few islanders put off with boats to trade fresh fish, fruit, and vegetables. We took aboard tuna, flounder that compared well with any I ever ate at home, mackerel, and little crayfish. There were good peaches and grapes. While the water casks were being cleaned out and refilled, Captain Shockley and the Mate went ashore with guns to try for some wild pigs and goats that roamed the hills. They didn't stay long. The glass dropped, and they came aboard quickly with two slaughtered pigs and a live nanny and billy goat. That night a gale of wind threatened to slam us against the rocks, so we hauled wind out of there.

Five days northwest of Juan Fernández the lookout raised something.

"Where away?" Captain Shockley shouted from the mizzen shrouds.

"Larboard, sir, about half mile off. Can't make out what 'tis."

We ran closer. Whatever it was, wasn't spouting. It looked like a couple hundred fish all thrashing the sea to foam.

"Right whale," the lookout sang out. "Fighting with blackfish!"

Now we could see! The whale must have been all of eighty feet. He was plunging and half breaching, lashing his flukes from eye to eye, while great black-and-white brutes, about twenty-five feet long, were tearing at him like sharks. Their heads were blunt and round, and they had big grinning mouths studded with double rows of vicious peg teeth. They dashed at the whale, throwing themselves at his head and ripping out lumps of blubber and meat big as casks. Once as he breached we made out three hanging like bulldogs to his lower jaw, while another was actually half inside his mouth.

"Boats away," Captain Shockley called. "We'll take some of those blackfish."

Our boats put off and we approached the riot of struggling monsters in the bloody water. I shipped my paddle and stood up as a couple of them darted under our bow like porpoises.

"Don't mess with the whale," Mr. Nanton called. "Just iron as many of them grampus as you can!"

They were all about us, their snouts greasy as they butted with the gluttony of pigs at the suffering whale. They took no notice of the boats, even colliding with us as they plunged at their prey. The whale lay there, blood pouring from dozens of wounds. His flukes lashed feebly, and under

water we could see his jaw hanging down and the killers nuzzling into his great mouth.

"They eat tongue only," Pete Brava said. "All grampus kill whale for is his tongue. Bloody cannibals, grampus!"

I darted my number one iron into one. It twisted like a snake and its head almost stove us. I ironed another and let them both wriggle while I reached for a lance. Jimmy Owen had the spare lance and was jabbing tirelessly. Mr. Nanton killed two with a boat spade. And still they took no notice of us. We tossed in a welter of foam and blood, jabbing the ferocious beasts like madmen. Last of all I lanced the two that still fought and wriggled to get at the whale, even though my irons were deep in them.

We hauled our catch back to the ship and went for more. By night there were thirty-odd blackfish alongside, and those left disappeared as they sounded after the sinking whale.

Now the sea was full of sharks, attracted by the blood. We had to fight them off with spades while we hauled the blackfish on board to strip off the blubber, rolling the carcasses over the larboard side and piling the blubber in the tryworks. We had to be careful; blackfish oil is precious and used only for lubricating fine watches and delicate instruments.

It was dawn before we had several dozen barrels of black-fish oil cooling and the deck swabbed down. The sea was scummy with blood and gurry for acres and still thick with long blue sharks, scavenging for the last bit of meat.

On we sailed until we hit a dead calm. The sea was like glass. From masthead we could see for miles, and there was nothing to break the endless glare of sun on water. For several days we were becalmed, our sails hanging down, the crew lying around under shade cloths, scratching at scrim-shaw, washing and mending, or just yarning. Captain Shockley was working a clever little lathe he'd made of whale teeth and pan bone for turning wood into spindles and chair legs.

When wind came again, we were on the grounds. At night we hove to and drifted. By day we tacked and sailed under short canvas to cover every inch of the grounds.

Inside a week we had taken four sperm, which kept us sweating day and night for two more days. But the hands were happy and telling each other this was a greasy cruise. And by the time we'd covered the Off Shore Grounds, our hold was full. So we headed for Honolulu to transship our oil.

We were glad to reach port. Our fresh food was long gone. Even the goats were eaten, for even this nanny refused to give the Captain milk for his coffee.

The consul came off and Captain Shockley reported the death of Stan Dunbar. We had an auction of his gear. There wasn't much of it: a pea jacket, reefer, torn oilskins, sea boots, some tattered shirts and underdrawers and a ditty box full of studs and things. But we bid high, for the money was to go home to his family. The Captain handed over a paper telling the amount for the consul to send home so Stan's mother could draw on the *Canton's* owners.

While the oil was being transshipped, some of us were given liberty. Owen got drunk and had to be bailed out of the jail. Nelson deserted. But there was no fuss about that. I think Captain Shockley had been thinking of paying him off anyhow, and his desertion just saved money.

But we cleared the port as soon as our oil was gone and pulled in at a tiny island to the west of the group where provisions and water were cheaper and there was mighty little chance for a liberty man to get into trouble. All we could see from the ship was a little village under stands of coco palms. Captain let our boat crew go ashore first—all except Jimmy Owen. We pulled like man-of-war men, rode the three walls of surf yelling like Indians, and pulled our boat up a steep white beach. The villagers came running with pineapples, pawpaws, and bananas and we gave them old trinkets we'd brought from the slop chest for the purpose of trading. There were mighty pretty girls with great brown eyes hanging flower wreaths around our necks. They wore red-and-white calico pareos given them by the missionaries. But, judging by their smiling and nodding and purring alongside a fellow, they hadn't paid much attention to the missionaries' talk.

I left the crew in the village and went off down the beach with Gene Brown; he took my old place as number one oar when George Leeds left our boat after I was promoted to boat steerer. Gene was a husky chap, about my own age, broad as a door, with fair hair and a solemn expression. He had a slow quiet voice and didn't say much unless he had something important to talk about. We got on well together.

Eating bananas, we wandered along the shore until we came to a trail inland. We followed it through dense undergrowth and over a hill. Then there was open country, dotted with trees.

"Hey, looky that," Gene said. "Horses! I haven't ridden a horse since I left home. Let's see if we can catch them."

I'd never been aboard a horse at all. But we crept up on two of them that were grazing under a shade tree. They reared back a bit when we caught their forelocks, but they seemed tame enough.

"Not much of a horse," Gene muttered as he swung aboard his. "Lookit those lumps!"

I got on mine somehow and there were great lumps on mine, too, under the hide of his neck and shoulders. But we had no time to puzzle. Those nags woke up as soon as they felt us on their backs, and set off at the rate of knots. We had no reins or tackle, so I hung on the mane while we galloped along a track over another hill and toward a cluster of little white huts and a larger building.

Someone saw us, and people in white shirts came out of the huts waving their arms and shouting. But the horses kept going.

"Looks like a farm," Gene shouted. "Maybe we'd better get off."

"Stay aboard," I said. "If we fall off, they'll catch us. Bring yours about and we'll make for the beach!"

But we couldn't turn them. Then two priests came out of the big hut and got ahead of us. The horses came about then and took us over the hill and back to the place we'd found them. They slowed to a walk and we slid off. Gene looked at them standing with their heads down and heaving. There was a queer smell about them.

"You suppose they're sick?" Gene said. "Look out! Someone coming!"

We ducked behind a thicket and saw a white man on another horse come cantering down. Behind him were several natives in white gowns, who grabbed the horses and started to lead them away.

"Did you see that?" Gene's face was yellow as cheese. "One of those fellows had no nose and some of his fingers were gone."

"Been in a fight, maybe," I said. "Let's get under way."

"Hey!" Gene whispered. "You know what this place is? I do. Those people are lepers. This is a leper station. I bet those horses have been used for experiments."

"Those lumps!"

"Maybe they've got leprosy, too. What'll we do?"

I looked at my shore-going clothes and felt mighty poorly.

"I'm getting these clothes off," I said.

We stripped with shaking hands and buried every stitch in the soft earth. Then we ran through the cover to the beach and scrubbed ourselves with sand and sea water until our bodies were raw. We waded along the shallows toward the village.

The natives saw us, and the rest of the boat crew came running and laughing fit to bust.

"What happen?" Big Olaf demanded. "You lose your duds?"

"We got to tell him," Gene whispered.

We got him to one side and told him what had happened. He jumped back like we'd pointed a gun at him.

"You can't go aboard," he said. "You'll give us all leprosy."

"We're scrubbed with sand," Gene faltered.

" 'Tain't enough," Olaf grunted. "Get behind them palms and wait."

We sat in the sand, shivering though it was still hot. After a while Olaf came with four bottles of native rum.

"All we had between us," he grumbled. "Now rub yourselves all over with this. That'll kill the poison if anything will. Don't say anything to the boat crew; they'll shoot you sooner than let you aboard."

We rubbed that drink into our inflamed skins until I screamed. Gene jumped up and down and swore his hide was on fire. We used all four bottles. I was almost drunk with the smell of it and there wasn't an inch of us that didn't blaze with agony.

"Don't wash it off," Olaf said. "Now get aboard. I told the hands you got your duds stole."

We crouched in the bow while the rest rowed us out to the *Canton.* There was laughter and remarks enough to last me to the end of my days, and when we crawled aboard, the Captain had a few things to say about young squirts who went swimming without leaving their clothes guarded, and came back stinking of rum.

That night we let buckets overside and made the cook heat them up. We scrubbed again with boiling water and yellow soap, and by morning we could hardly stand the touch of clothing on us. Every day for several weeks we looked each other over like mother monkeys for signs of leprosy. But we never caught it, and I've been thankful to Olaf ever since.

We cleared that island the next day, and I was mighty glad no one came to see who'd been fooling with their sick horses.

Two days later we raised a lone sperm bull. Our boat was first away, and I got fast to him with one iron. Then the ride started. He sounded and took almost all our line. Then he breached almost a quarter-mile away, and we hauled like slaves while Owen flaked down the line. I changed ends with Mr. Nanton as we closed on the resting animal. We bowed in. But as soon as the lance touched him, he went mad, rolling over and over until the line was wrapped about him like a Christmas package and our starboard gunwale was under water. We paid out line and he took it until there was no more than five or six turns in the tub. Then he jawed back, chopping just ahead of our bow, every jerk dragging us closer to those murderous teeth. Mr. Nanton tried again to lance him. But the lance drew and he sounded again.

Somehow the line must have slid off him, for it came aboard in a tangle. We hauled again when he breached, the line in a man-killing hurrah's nest in the stern sheets.

"I'll get him this time," the Mate panted. "Bow me in. Lively now! Wood to black skin!"

He set the lance three feet abaft the eye fin. The whale

flurried and lashed with his flukes until I thought he'd founder us. Then he ran again on the surface, the line jumping over the thwarts in tangled loops. And one of them took Mr. Nanton's arm and flipped him overboard before he could even shout.

"Man overboard!" I yelled. "Cut!" I figured the slack line would let him free.

The whale turned right ahead of us and the line went slack before Gene Brown, in the bow, could cut it.

"Haul away!" I screamed. "Maybe he's still fast."

The whale was on our starboard side, spouting pink. We hauled line until Mr. Nanton, his arm and chest fouled in the line, showed under water. We dragged him aboard and freed him. Then I signaled one of the other boats to take our line; we had to get Mr. Nanton back to the ship. He lay in the stern, his arm at a queer angle and blood all over him. Coffin's boat took our line and went in to finish our whale. We made for the *Canton*. Mr. Nanton was sitting up, spitting sea water and cussing by the time we pulled alongside.

We got him on board, but his legs wouldn't hold him until Captain Shockley gave him a jorum of brandy. Then he made it below, blood running down his side from where the line had cut him. His arm was broken in two places, but the Captain set it. That night he was sitting on the afterhouse watching us trying out his whale, and he with his arm in a sling for a week or two.

That's how I came to be Captain's boat steerer. George Leeds was promoted to Third Mate; Coffin, to Second; Reynolds, to Mr. Nanton's place, and Nanton to act as sailing master so the Captain could lower whales. Big Olaf took my place as Mate's boat steerer.

"Mr. Nanton was lucky at that," Captain Shockley told

me while I was at the helm next day. "I've seen a man come up in two pieces after being towed by a whale. There was one captain, though, fought a whale single-handed with nothing but a sheath knife. Lived, too."

I wondered about that one. My uncle said he had heard the story from a man who had seen it.

"The Second Mate of this ship had fastened to a right whale," he started. "Now, a right whale fights with his flukes, cutting them like scythes 'from eye to eye' as we say. Anyway, the Second Mate's boat couldn't bow in to kill him. So the Captain ordered his boat to fasten, changed ends, bowed in right over the flukes, and lanced him. His trick with right whales was to lance downward from over the shoulder; that's the quickest way to reach his life. But the Captain's lance went into the shoulder blade and stuck. He couldn't draw it, and that whale shuddered all over. Then he cut flukes, hit the Captain's boat broadside, and stove her. Captain cut the line to save being towed under and swam with the rest of his crew to hang on to what was left of their boat.

"The Second Mate wanted to cut and pick them up.

" 'Hold fast,' the Captain shouted. 'We're all right. Kill that danged whale.'

"It was at that moment the whale breached right under them and sent men and wreckage high in the air. They came down yelling, and the mighty mass of whale fell right on them. Two were killed then and there; never saw them again. The Captain tried to swim away through the bloody water, but the whale was rolling and churning with his flukes to smash the floating wreckage. It was as though the whale was looking for them, feeling with his snout through the sea. The Captain swam hard as he could for the Second Mate's boat, which had cut by now, when he saw that whale coming straight for him. He dived, felt something brush by, and held on to a line that was fast to one of the irons in the whale. He let him tow him until he thought himself clear of the wreckage, dived deep to avoid the flukes, and surfaced.

"But the whale had turned and saw the swimming man. He came at him, breached high, and dropped right on him. The Captain, stunned, was driven deep. Half drowning, he came to the surface. Again there was a mighty wash of water, the black shape above and the thunderous crash as the head of the whale came down beside him.

"Bewildered, he tried to swim away. The great body slid past. Desperately he grabbed an iron that jutted from the side of the whale. Immediately he cut flukes, caught the Captain an awful blow on the legs, and knocked him clear.

"Floundering desperately, he saw the Second Mate's boat coming down to him. But the whale saw it too, and made for it, slapping the water with his great flukes until the boat crew, scared out of their wits, pulled back toward the ship.

"The whale turned, saw the Captain, and again dropped on him. He could no longer use his legs. He dog-paddled, sinking each time the brute breached. Then he remembered the tender tip of a right whale's snout and managed to get out his sheath knife. Next time the whale came feeling for him, he drove the blade into his nose. The animal backed, rolled past, and tried to slap the Captain flat with his flukes. But he dived again. The last thing the Captain remembered was driving the knife into a round whitish lump the size of a basketball on the end of the whale's snout.

"Then the Mate, who was chasing another whale, saw distress signals from the ship. He pulled back and found the shipkeeper trying to sail the vessel between the Captain and the whale.

" 'Heave to,' the Mate ordered. 'You'll tear him to pieces with her sheathing.'

"So he called his men to pull for the Captain. The whale made for the Mate's boat too, but the men pulled hard and he managed to get the Captain by the collar and haul him aboard before the whale could reach them. Then they rowed back to the ship and lifted their unconscious Captain on board.

" 'Back to the whale,' the Mate ordered. 'He's too cussed dangerous to leave.'

"They pulled close, fastened, and the Mate lanced him right over the shoulder. The exhausted whale spouted blood high and sank in a violent stream of bubbles from his punctured lungs.

"The Captain kept to his bunk with bruises and lacerations for several weeks. Then he was up again and lowering with the rest of them.

"And when you go hunting right whales," Captain Shockley finished, "there's a few things to remember. You can back a right whale, even if he's charging your boat, by pricking him on the tip of the snout. He'll sound under your boat, turn, or even come about. But watch out for his flukes if he does. Another thing. Don't lance a right whale downward from over the shoulder. What's the use of risking your neck for a sunk whale?"

XII.

I AM MADE A BOAT HEADER

I hamstring a whale and am almost killed . . . Fin out! . . . The whaleship log . . . Promoted to Third Mate . . . I leave the Canton.

I MADE ONLY ONE lowering as boat steerer in the Captain's boat. For after that once, when I fastened to a fifty-two-barrel sperm, changed ends, and watched him lance the creature, he stayed in the stern of the boat.

"You don't want to be a boat steerer and live in the steerage all your life," he said. "And you can't join the afterguard until you've learned to lance a whale and head your boat."

I got my first lesson some three hundred miles W.S.W. of the Sandwich Islands. We had lowered on a likely sperm bull—not too big but mighty lively. We had peaked our oars and were coming up to him under paddles when he suddenly pitchpoled—just stood on his flukes with his head sticking straight up, bobbing and milling around to look us over.

" 'Pears like he's readying for trouble," Bow Oar said.

I'd never seen a whale behave the way that bull did. As we closed, he reversed, stood on his head, and lobtailed;

Fast to a whale

thrashed the water with his flukes until we were pitching in a welter of foam. It was as though he warned us to keep our distance. Then he swam away, not fast, not alarmed, going easily, spout, hump, sound, spout, hump, sound. We caught him in five risings, and I darted two irons into him.

Then the fun started. He sounded deep, the line going straight down, flake after flake. It slacked, and we were hauling in fast as we could when he breached astern of us. Captain Shockley whipped us about and clear of the line or the bull would have capsized us. Then he charged, the rocklike head well out of the water and the narrow underjaw scooping up the sea. Again the Captain swept us out of danger and the whale shot past, the flukes lifting and smashing down not a fathom from the boat. He sounded again, breached a few boat lengths ahead, and started running. I never thought a whale could go so fast. Our bow was down and the waves shooting up each side of me like the wings of a giant bird. And every time we hit a roller, the shock almost knocked me off the standing cleats. But the line was taut as a bar, all hands holding fast, and we could do nothing but run.

The *Canton* was hull down before he slowed and lay on the surface, spouting fast and furious. This was the time for us to change ends. I looked aft.

"You take him, Lester," said the Captain, cool as a cucumber.

I felt about ten feet tall! I was a boat header, now, in full command. I felt a mite queer, too; I was also responsible for the lives of all on board. I tried not to show anything; just knocked the guard off a lance, drew it from its beckets, and got myself set.

We hauled up slowly, so as not to gally him. The black flukes, three times the beam of our boat, lay just under the keel. If he'd chosen, just then, he could have flipped us into the air like you'd flip a coin. But we slid past.

"Bow me in," I said, quietly as I could.

The boat rocked in his wash until his hump raised above us like a sea wall. For a second there was silence except for the steady whistling gush of his spout. I took a deep breath, rested the leaf-shaped lance head against the black skin and shoved. It was a queer sensation; the blade went in like into butter, and the whole five-foot shaft disappeared. I started to churn. He jumped and tore the lance from my grip. But I snatched the warp and drew it free. Then he was gone, rolling under us until the Captain yelled, "Stern all," and swept us clear.

The bull came up on his back, jaw out and snapping. I saw now why he fought that way; his eyes are closer to his belly than to his back and he could see us better. His head bumped us. The jaw that had been right over us like a jagged boom clashed shut, but we were half a length away. The flukes lifted and knocked the three peaked starboard oars high into the air, luckily not hitting anyone. They smashed down again. We were blinded by spray and all hands yelling like Indians. I had my lance back, bent the soft iron shaft straight and wiped the water from my eyes. The Captain heaved us around and we headed straight for him, still on his back, tail and jaw out of the water.

"Now!" Captain Shockley shouted.

The jaw crashed shut, and we were almost riding over him. I jammed the lance under his eye fin and shoved it in as hard as I could. The way of the boat drew it out. He rolled right under us as we pulled clear in a flurry of spray and tangled line.

"Once more and we've got him!"

It wasn't that easy. The bull was gallied, rolling, breaching, and humping in his agony. He came at us again, and it wasn't until his scarred head was almost over us that the Captain heaved us to one side, like a bullfighter dodging a charge.

The whale slid past so quickly I couldn't use the lance, and his flukes smashed down so close we were half swamped. But there was no time to bail. He came about to charge again. Just before he reached us, he sounded.

"Back. Starn all!" The Captain shouted, heaving on the steering sweep. The bull breached right alongside and rolled. But his wash carried us clear. Then he ran again.

I remembered something I'd heard the boat steerers yarning about. It's a trick to bring a spade down on the small of a running whale and cut the fluke tendons. If it works, he is helpless. If you miss, it's a stove boat and dead men. I took a quick look aft. Stroke Oar was bailing. The Captain, blinded by spray, was yelling to us to close, and the crew were paddling like demons. I was too excited to have any sense. I drew out the chisel-edged spade and called for more speed. We slammed after him and he slowed.

"Bow in!" I yelled.

He was humping as we rode over the flukes. In a second he would toss them and sound. I sighted on the root of the flukes and stabbed downward. I felt resistance and jabbed again. Next thing I knew I was in the water.

I came up choking with brine, blood, and slick. I tried to swim, but the seas kept breaking over me. I turned on my back to float. A sea lifted me, and I saw the boat at some distance. I yelled, and they ran down to me.

"We're cut," Bow Oar said as they dragged me aboard. "But he's anchored."

I got to my place and we pulled to where the whale lay spouting pink, his stern in a cloud of bloody water. He rolled a little, and I could see his jaw snapping under the surface. They bowed me in and I drove the lance deep. He jerked, rolled, and snapped his jaws madly. He went into a convulsion, bowed like a trout, and thick blood gushed from his spout. Then he rolled, fin out.

We lay alongside the whale for three hours until the *Canton* ran down to us.

"You ought to have your ears cut off," the Captain said while we were waiting. "Hamstringing a fighting whale! Might have got us all killed!"

But I could see he wasn't really angry. And the boat crew were grinning. We had us a good sixty-barrel whale which was worth all the risks.

I found myself a bit of a hero when we went on board after securing the sperm. The boat steerers made a big fuss of me, and I felt mighty big-headed. But to myself I made up my mind I'd never try it again unless I had to. I had the shakes all that night, thinking of what might have happened if I hadn't—more by luck than good gumption—slashed the tendons that governed those man-killing flukes.

In the next three months I lanced eight whales from the Captain's boat. Then he let me head her alone, with Tom Gardner, who had been Bow Oar, as boat steerer. We managed pretty well; the crew worked like a machine, and within a fifth month our hold was full of oil again.

On the way back to Honolulu to transship, Captain Shockley called me to his cabin. It was the first time I'd been below the quarter-deck. I stood in the narrow space, keeping my dirty clothes clear of the blue plush settee that was built onto the transom, and dodging the brass lamp that hung in gimbals from a deck beam.

"Sit down, Lester," Captain Shockley said, taking a cigar from a locker.

I did so, feeling mighty peculiar. I knew I'd done nothing wrong; he'd have cussed me out on deck if I had. So what was this?

"How old are you?" He grunted through puffs of fragrant smoke.

"Going on eighteen, sir," I said.

"Young for a boat header, these days. Though I was a third mate at seventeen; been to sea five years. Well, you've grown a mite and you've filled out. I hear you can take care of yourself in a bobbery."

"Yes, sir."

"Well, you've got a lot to learn, still, and don't forget it."

"No, sir."

He flipped open a big ledger.

"This is a logbook—an account of the days and doings aboard ship. Here's how you write it up."

I read, next to a wide margin:

Lat; 18 Deg 26 Min N.
Long; 165 Deg 28½ Min W.
Sunday, Nov. 9.

This day begins with strong breeze and light rain squalls. Ship running before the wind. Took in jib fore-topgallant, foretop and mainsails. Course N.E.E. In later watch wind moderated but heavy swell. So ends this day.

There were some interesting designs in the margin.

"You could have made yourself a set of these," Captain Shockley said. "These are symbols used every time a whale is sighted. So you can see at a glance how we fared. This one"—he pointed—"flukes down, means a whale sighted but not lowered on.

Illustrations in a whaler's logbook

"This shows when you lower.

"This means sperm and the number of barrels he made.

"Same for a right whale.

"Grampus.

"This when a whale draws iron and escapes.

"Usually we carve these stamps out of wood and make scrimshaw handles for them, like this."

He showed me a mahogany case, the lid inlaid with a sperm whale of tooth ivory. It was lined with green baize, and inside were all the stamps, each in its properly shaped place, every one with a beautifully carved sperm tooth handle.

"Made them when I was eighteen," Captain Shockley said softly.

I made up my mind I'd have a set of symbols before I became a whale captain. I'd carve them myself, too, each one different and each one of the whitest sperm teeth.

From that day until we reached Honolulu it was my duty to write up the log. I also had to learn how to shoot the sun and find our position by dead reckoning; that and learning the planets was harder work than killing a whale.

By the time we reached Oahu I still didn't have it down pat. But I could take a sight and work out a position with chronometer and log. That, Captain Shockley said, would do me for the time being.

There were five other whaleships at anchor, all of them outward bound, waiting for provisions and to recruit Kanaka hands. To the surprise of some, Captain Shockley allowed us all shore leave, even Jimmy Owen.

"I'm not worried," I heard him tell Mr. Nanton, who was up and over his broken arm. "We've had one of the best cruises the *Canton* ever made. I'll lose no hands this side of New Bedford."

But he lost one hand. Me!

We were empty and almost ready to put to sea again when he called me aft.

"Lester," he said. "I got to get rid of you."

Also signalized bark virginia of New Bedford. At night under Lat 18=34 S Long 91=48 W

H & L — VIRGINIA — easy sail — HYDASPE

24th *Tuesday*

Strong breezes in the former. Latter moderate. At 8 oclock saw a school of sperm whales. with Killers. Blackfish & cowfish. lowered 2 boats but

VALPARAISO.   VIRGINIA.   A. HOUGHTON

whales was going like a race horse to windward. I did catch one. At night gamming with barks A Hought... 2 Valparaiso 700 bbls, & virginia. 650 bbls. After gamming stee... Lat 19=13 S Long 92=22 W

You could have knocked me down with a hank of spun yarn.

"What have I done, sir?" I asked. "I thought you were satisfied with me."

"I am, boy. I'm proud of you. And that's it. But this is a fair ship. What'll the hands think if I discharge an officer to make a man third mate on his first cruise? My own nephew, too!"

"Couldn't I stay boat steerer, sir?"

"No. You rate the afterguard. Trouble is, there's no place in our afterguard for you."

"Do I have to go home, sir?" I mumbled.

I felt sick. I'd seen hard times with the *Canton*, but I had good friends aboard her, fore and aft. It seemed to me then that I'd never known any life but that of my first ship. She *was* my home.

"Look out the stern window," he said. "That's the bark *Deborah*, Captain Crichton, out of New Bedford. She's bound for the Japan Grounds. Captain Crichton's shy a third mate. He'll take you at a fiftieth lay. What with the money you've earned aboard the *Canton* and what you'll receive from the *Deborah*—if you bring them the luck you've brought us—you'll have a tidy sum when you reach home port. I advise you to ship in the *Deborah*."

What could I do? I was learning another lesson. The life of a whaleman is one of partings, and friendships last only as long as each cruise.

They rowed me over to the *Deborah* in style; Gene Brown, Big Olaf, Jimmy Owen, George Leeds, and Pete Brava. I shook their hands and wished them luck. I was an officer now. Maybe it was better I was in a different vessel; I wouldn't have liked to come the afterguard over my foremast friends of the *Canton*.

She sailed next day. I watched her roll across the lovely bay of Honolulu, her smoky sails dark against the blue sky.

"Greasy luck, *Canton*," I whispered.

That was the last I saw of her, her crew or my uncle, Captain Shockley, for many a year. I was glad none of the *Deborah* hands could see their new Third Mate with tears in his eyes.

"A dead whale or a stove boat."
Inscription on the Whaleman's Statue
in New Bedford, Massachusetts

GLOSSARY

GLOSSARY OF OLD WHALING TERMS

AFTERHOUSE——Shelter over wheel, galley, and companion to captain's quarters in stern of whaleship.

ALOW FROM ALOFT——Order calling lookouts down from masthead.

AMBERGRIS——Waxy foreign matter found in alimentary canal of sperm whale; used in making perfume.

ARTICLES——Ship's papers which all hands must sign.

BARREL——Measure of oil; 31½ gallons. Oil is stored in great casks.

BECKET——Rope loop.

BLANKET PIECE——Sheet of blubber cut from scarf as it is torn from whale.

BLUBBER——Thick fibrous coating of whale. Full of oil, it is insulation against cold and pressure.

BOAT STEERER——Harpooner. He fastens to whale, then changes places with boat header and steers until whale is killed.

BOOK——Horse pieces cut into chunks and sliced so that blubber is attached to skin like the leaves of a book. Sliced extra thin, they are called bibles.

BREACH––When whale leaps almost clear of the water.

CASE––Forehead of sperm whale.

CLUMSY CLEAT––Plank athwart, bow of boat. The edge is notched to fit harpooner's thigh and steady him while darting.

CRAFT––Harpoons, spades, lances–anything made of iron or steel.

CRANES––Timber brackets that swing out under davits and support boats.

CRESSET––Iron basket filled with blazing scrap. Used as torch while trying-out at night.

CUT FLUKES––Sweep the flukes from side to side in fighting.

CUTTING IN––Stripping blubber from whale.

DART––To heave, pitch, or toss the harpoon.

DONKEY'S BREAKFAST––Cornhusk or straw filling for whaleman's mattress.

DRAW––When a harpoon pulls out of a whale.

FIN OUT––Position of a dead whale (on his side with eye fin out of the water).

FLAKE––Complete turn of rope in a coil.

FLAKE DOWN––Prepare line for running. It is coiled with end up, then coiled down on the end so that each flake overlaps the preceding one so as to run out without tangling.

FLUKES––The horizontal tail of a whale.

FLURRY––Death struggle of whale. He thrashes his flukes, lists to one side, and swims in a circle in a last try to escape. Finally there is a convulsion, he spouts blood and floats, fin out.

FOUL LINE––Whale line that has kinked and looped around something or someone in the boat.

GALLIED––Scared.

GALLOWS––Structure over midship deck to support spare boats.

GAM––A visit and exchange of boats between whaleships far at sea. A talk or bull session.

GEAR––All whaleboat equipment that is not made of iron.

GREENIE––Hand on his first voyage.

GROUNDS––Areas where whales are regularly found.

GURRY––Spilled oil, slime, blood, refuse that smears a whaleship deck during trying-out.

HARDTACK——Thick square biscuit, baked like dog biscuit to make it last.

HEAD TO HEAD——To attack a whale headfirst.

HEAD MATTER——Spermaceti, which comes from the case, or head, of a sperm whale.

HEN FRIGATE——Whaleship with a woman aboard; captains sometimes took their wives along.

HOLIDAY——The part of a job that is not done properly, like a spot of dirt left behind something.

HOOPS——A pair of rings bolted to the mastheads for the purpose of supporting and steadying the lookouts.

HORSE PIECE——Strip of blubber about six inches wide, sliced from the blanket piece.

HUMP——Dorsal fin of a sperm or humpback whale.

IRON——A harpoon.

JAW BACK——When a sperm whale rolls on his back to fight with his jaw.

LARBOARD——The port, or left side, of a ship facing for'ard. Only used aboard whaleships.

LAY——Share of the ship's earnings. A long lay is the smallest share; a short lay is the biggest share, usually the captain's.

LIFE——Vulnerable spot of a whale, usually the lungs.

LINE——Equator.

LOBSCOUSE——Stew made of salt beef, crumbled hardtack, vegetables, and anything handy.

LOBTAIL——When sperm whale beats the surface with his flukes.

LOGGERHEAD——Upright post in stern of boat for snubbing the whale line.

LONG LAY——See LAY.

MILL——The swift turning around and around of a whale. Usually means he's looking for trouble.

MONKEY JACKET——Short coat. No long coats allowed in boats.

MONKEY ROPE——Line knotted about a man's waist to lower him overside and keep him safe.

MOUNT——Secure harpoon or lance to its pole.

NANTUCKET SLEIGH RIDE——A ride in a boat that is towed by a gallied whale.

NIB——The tender tip of a right whale's snout.

PAN BONE——Flat slabs of bone from root of sperm whale's jaw.

PEAKED OAR——When a boat is fast to a whale the handles of the oars are jammed into holes near the floor of the boat. They stick up far enough to clear rough water and form a *V* which guides the whale line down the center of the boat.

PITCHPOLE——When a whale stands on his tail, bobbing up and down with his head out of the water.

POD——School, or herd, of whales.

RED FLAG——When whale spouts blood.

RISING——When whale surfaces to spout.

SALT HORSE, SALT JUNK——Corned beef that has been soaked, sometimes for years, in brine.

SAVE-ALL——Scoop or cask for oil and gurry that has been spilled.

SCARF——The long strip of blubber that is torn from the whale the way a scarf is unwound.

SCRAP——Blubber from which the oil has been boiled. Used for fuel in the tryworks fires.

SCRIMSHAW——The whaleman's spare-time art. The only true American folk art save that of the Indians.

SEA PIG——Porpoise.

SHORT LAY——See LAY.

SLICK——Oily patch left on surface when whale sounds.

SLOP CHEST——Ship's store, where whalemen can buy clothing, tobacco, knives, etc.

SMALL——Slender part of whale next to flukes.

SNUB——Check the whaleline by taking turns about the loggerhead.

SOUND——Dive under water.

SPERMACETI——Head matter of sperm whale. The best quality. In the old days, used to make candles; now, for ointments and beauty preparations.

SPIRACLE——Spout hole.

SPRING——Row hard.

SQUID——Octopus, cuttlefish; sperm whale's food.

STERN ALL——Order to back the boat from danger.

STOVE——To smash a boat.

STRIKE——To fasten to whale with harpoon.

SWEEP FLUKES——Whale lifts flukes from water and sweeps them in fighting "from eye to eye."

THIEF——Cylinder small enough to enter bunghole of a cask and take out a cup of water.

TOSS FLUKES——Raise flukes from water, usually before sounding.

TRYING OUT——Boiling the oil from blubber.

WAIF——Flag on sharpened staff, stuck as marker in dead whale.

WHITE HORSE——The bloodless meat in a sperm whale's forehead.

WHITE-WATER——Spray and foam made by breaching whale.

WOOD TO BLACK SKIN——When the bow of a boat collides with the slimy hide of a whale.

PICTURE CREDITS